RHS GARDEN EXPLORERS HANDBOOK

Written by
Naomi Slade and Simon Maughan

This Book Belongs to:

. . . .

First published in 2007 by

The Royal Horticultural Society

80 Vincent Square
London SW1P 2PE

Registered Charity number 222879

www.rhs.org.uk

RHS Garden Explorers' Handbook

A CIP catalogue record for this book is available from
the British Library.

ISBN 978-1-902896-76-2

Edited by Simon Maughan
Designed by Alison Gadsby and Clair Stutton
Printed and bound in the UK by Friary Press, Dorset

Contents

Introduction

Are you ready to become an RHS Garden Explorer?

Ricky, Hannah, and Sam are already Garden Explorers, and they spend most of their free time exploring every inch of their gardens with their creature friends: Bizzie Bea, Lady Dotty, and Wiggles Worm.

Join them and other friends all through this book as they help you discover all you need to know about plants, garden animals, and gardening.

Just get started as soon as you are ready with any of the spring, summer, autumn, or winter activities, and you can become a Garden Explorer too!

Meet Ricky

Ricky is seven years old and lives next door to Hannah and Sam. He's always digging holes with one of his brightly coloured spades, and his next garden project is to dig the biggest hole in the world so that he can plant the biggest tree!

Once he dug up an old vase and told everyone it was Roman, but Hannah turned it upside down and it said China on the bottom in big red letters. Ooops.

Meet Hannah

Hannah is eight and three quarters and likes to think she's the one in charge of almost everything, especially the vegetable patch.

Her favourite thing is to watch the vegetables grow. She thinks that by talking to them they will grow even quicker and often crouches down next to them to tell them stories. This always makes the boys laugh out loud, although if the truth be known, they love listening to what she has to say.

Hannah loves being with her brother, Sam, and her next door neighbour, Ricky, even though she makes out she doesn't.

Meet Sam

Sam is Hannah's brother. He is only five but he thinks he's eleven. He always wants to climb the biggest trees, but Hannah says he has to do as he's told. His favourite job in the garden is the 'weed hunt'.

The garden for him is like an adventure playground with lots of fun things to do and discover. He enjoys nothing more than to collect worms and dangle them in front of Hannah's face. He also loves using a magnifying glass to spy on insects in the garden.

Meet Bizzie Bea

Bizzie Bea is always busy, buzzing busily around the garden. Her favourite garden is at number 23 where Hannah and Sam live. That garden has masses of lavender, which is one of her favourites.

Meet Lady Dotty

Lady Dotty takes great pride in her bright red back and black spots and likes to show off her beauty around the garden. She is a true lady and works hard to look after and help the others, which wins her many friends in the garden.

She's best known for her enthusiastic efforts to eat greenfly from in and around the flowerbed.

Meet Wiggles Worm

Wiggles Worm is always wiggling and poking his head out of the soil to see what's going on. Sam often picks him up and takes him on little trips to the end of the garden, which are quite fun. His ambition is to eventually make it over to the compost heap.

Best of all, Wiggles loves being in the dark soil and chomping the little bits that no-one else can see.

Daffodil

Daffodils are such bright and cheerful plants that people like to plant them everywhere. There are orange ones, yellow ones, white ones, and sometimes the colours are mixed up. Write down three different types you have seen and where you saw them growing:

Narcissus

Where	When	What colour were the flowers?
1.		
2.		
3.		
4.		

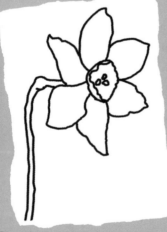

Colour in the daffodil above and then stick a photo here of a similar one that you have spotted.

Fact: Daffodils are poisonous. Don't eat them!

Bluebell

One of the wonders of the British countryside is a bluebell wood in full flower. You have to see it to believe it! Unfortunately, the English bluebell is under threat from the Spanish bluebell. If the spread of the Spanish bluebell is not halted, it might take over the English countryside!

Hyacinthus

Copy the images below to learn to spot the differences between English and Spanish bluebells

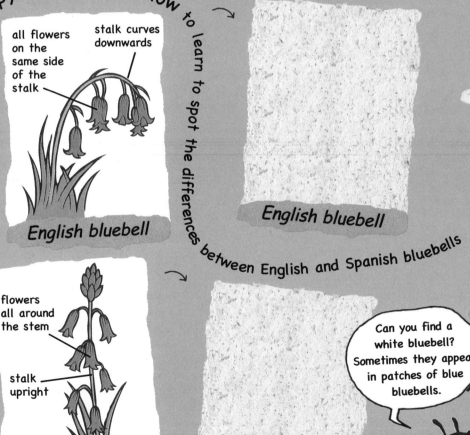

all flowers on the same side of the stalk

stalk curves downwards

English bluebell

English bluebell

flowers all around the stem

stalk upright

Spanish bluebell

Spanish bluebell

Can you find a white bluebell? Sometimes they appear in patches of blue bluebells.

7

Hazel

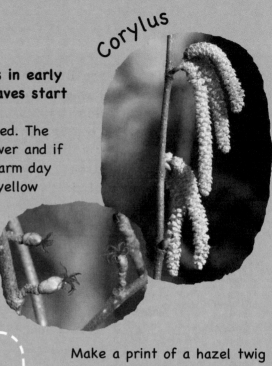

Corylus

Hazel trees produce catkins in early spring, long before their leaves start to come out.

Hazel trees are wind pollinated. The catkin is the tree's male flower and if you tap a ripe catkin on a warm day you will see a little puff of yellow pollen grains. The pollen fertilizes the tiny red female flowers that then grow on to become nuts later in the year.

Make a print of a hazel twig by painting it and pressing onto a piece of paper, then stick it in here:

← Can you see where the leaves are going to grow? Draw an arrow to mark the leaf buds. Add some yellow catkins and red flowers.

DID YOU KNOW pollen contains lots of protein, which makes it good food for hungry bees when they wake up after winter and there is not much to eat.

Fact: The sort of pollen that causes hay fever mostly comes from wind-pollinated plants like grasses and some trees.

Hawthorn

Hawthorn trees are gnarly and exciting. In May, the blossom made up of thousands of tiny flowers looks like a frothy white foam covering trees and hedgerows. They have pretty red berries in autumn. It is the only British plant to be named after the month in which it flowers.

Crataegus

The faces of green men are tree spirits. They are sometimes carved onto churches and are often wreathed in hawthorn. Some pubs are named 'The Green Man' – can you find one? Here is a picture of a green man.

Can you design your own?

FACT:

Young hawthorn leaves are edible and are called 'bread and cheese leaves' by country children.

DID YOU KNOW it is supposed to be bad luck to bring hawthorn indoors.

Primrose

Primroses can often be seen in woods and on banks in spring. The wild ones are pale yellow, but the cultivated types can be all sorts of colours and are known as primulas, polyanthus, or auriculas.

Primula

pin-type primrose

Primrose flowers can either be 'pin' or 'thrum' – see opposite. Look closely into the eye of the flowers to see!

'Pin' flowers have what appears to be a pinhead in the middle of the eye. It is actually the female part of the flower, called the stigma (see page 40).

Plant up a small pot with primulas to go on your windowsill

Paint a picture of it or take a photograph and stick it in here:

thrum-type primrose

DID YOU KNOW
The primrose gets its name from 'prima rosa' - the 'first flower of the year'.

FACT: Primrose can be used as a girl's name

Forsythia

Forsythia

Bushes of forsythia burst into flower in early spring, while they are still without leaves. They create a splash of brilliant yellow in the garden. Forsythias are named after Mr William Forsyth who helped found the Royal Horticultural Society in 1804.

Forsythia has lots of flowers on side shoots all the way down its long, arching branches. How many can you count on one branch? . . . .

You will notice the new shoots emerging from the buds. These will carry next year's flowers. So if you are going to give your forsythia bush a trim (gardeners call this 'pruning') do it now, so the plant has all summer to grow new shoots. If you prune too late, your forsythia may not flower next year. **This is true for all spring-flowering shrubs!**

Imagine you are Mr Forsyth and you have gone on an intrepid plant-collecting trip to wild bandit-country in China. Write a letter to your scientist friends describing the plant you have just found and stick it in here:

Folklore - Is it Still True?

Here are some proverbs, old sayings that tell you how to predict the weather.

"Red sky at night, shepherds delight; Red sky in the morning, shepherds warning".

This proverb suggests that if there is a red sunset then the weather will be good the next day.

Do you think gardeners should be pleased if the sky is red at night? Can you find out if it is true?

THIS MORNING THE SKY WAS RED.

Date: . . . .

The weather this afternoon was:

. . . .

TONIGHT THE SKY WAS RED

Date: . . . .

The weather the next day was:

. . . .

"Oak before ash, expect a splash; ash before oak, expect a soak".

oak leaf

ash leaf

This saying is about which of the two trees gets its leaves first in the spring. If the ash leaves come out first, it is supposed to rain a lot.

FIND AN ASH TREE AND AN OAK TREE NEAR YOUR HOUSE.

Which comes into leaf first? . . . .

Has it been cold and wet, or hot and dry recently? . . . .

Is this is a good way to forecast the weather? Why?

. . . .

. . . .

Spring

"Rain before seven, shine by eleven".

This saying says that if it is wet when you wake up, then by eleven o'clock the sun should be shining. Does it work? Does it work the other way around too, if it is sunny early in the morning?

Record your results over three days here:

DAY ONE
Date:
When I woke up the weather was: . . . .
By lunchtime the weather
was: . . . .

DAY TWO
Date:
When I woke up the weather was: . . . .
By lunchtime the weather
was: . . . .

DAY THREE
Date:
When I woke up the weather was: . . . .
By lunchtime the weather
was: . . . .

What do you conclude from this? Is the saying true, or are they making it up?

. . . .

. . . .

The garden needs it to rain sometimes. Too much dry weather makes the plants thirsty and they will need watering.

Can you invent a weather-predicting proverb of your own?

. . . .

. . . .

Some plants come from hot, dry places and don't get much rain water.

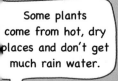

. . . .while others like to have their feet in the water most of the time.

Germinate Some Seeds!

A seed is a small packet of food, enclosed by a hard, protective coat. Each one can grow into a new plant. They can remain 'asleep' in the soil for years, until the conditions are right for them to sprout and grow; all that is needed is a bit of water, sunshine and some sort of soil to grow in.

SEEDS TO TRY: Lettuce, mustard, cress, marigolds, tomatoes, pumpkins, cabbages, sunflowers, courgettes, and broad beans.

YOU COULD ALSO GROW a cut-and-come again salad mixture in a pot. Let the salad seeds grow, then trim them with scissors when they have a few leaves. They will grow back again.

1. Place 2 sheets of paper towel on a small plate or dish. Wet the paper and place 5–10 of your dried seeds onto it. Put it on a warm, sunny windowsill in a clear plastic bag (do not let it touch the seeds). Draw your seeds here:

Plants must have water to germinate and grow.

2. Keep the paper towel moist by watering each day. While watering, observe the seeds. Use the table on the opposite page to record what happens. How many days does it take the seeds to break open and grow a sprouting shoot? Draw what happens here:

Plants use sunlight to make food!

3. How many days does it take the seedling to turn green and form its first leaves? The seed has now turned into a seedling. Draw one to show what it looks like. Don't forget to draw the root, which has very fine hairs to help it take up water.

4. Keep the seedlings in the light and continue to water them. How long does it take for the next set of leaves to appear? These are first set of 'true leaves'. Draw the shape of these true leaves in the space opposite. They are different for every type of plant.

Use the ruler on the side of this page to measure your seedlings

5. Your seedling is now a small plant. Grow it on by planting it in a small pot of compost.

	No. of seeds geminated	How tall is the tallest?	How many leaves on tallest seedling?
Day 1			
Day 3			
Day 5			
Day 7			
Day 13			
Day 17			

12cm
11cm
10cm
9cm
8cm
7cm
6cm
5cm
4cm
3cm
2cm
1cm

Make an Easter Tree

Easter is a great time to get out in the garden. The weather is warming up and everything is beginning to grow. Brighten up the garden by decorating some eggs to hang on bare branches, and think about places to hide eggs for an Easter egg hunt.

You will need:
- A nice twiggy branch
- Some eggs and a bowl
- String
- A long needle
- Paints, thick ready-mixed ones are best
- A paintbrush
- Tray of sand to stand the finished eggs in while they dry (optional).

CAUTION!
Ask a grown-up to help you

1. Make holes in both ends of each egg using the needle – ask a grown-up to help you as needles are very sharp. The hole in the bottom end of each egg should be bigger than hole in the pointy end.

2. Hold the egg firmly in your hand over the bowl, taking care not to squeeze, and blow through the smaller hole so that the runny egg comes out through the bottom hole.

> You can make scrambled egg with the runny egg that you blow out of the shell.

3. Tie a knot in one end of a piece of string and feed the string through the larger hole then the smaller hole so the egg can be hung up.

4. Paint the egg and hang it from your branch when it is dry.

What sort of tree did your branch come from?

Write its name here (see page 96 for some help)

. . . .

You could use its fruit and flowers for ideas when painting your eggs: apple blossom and apples, catkins and hazel nuts, cherries, or even the birds who might nest in it. Look at the colours of its leaves, flowers, or bark, and use them to design a pattern.

Have a go at decorating your own eggs on the tree below.

Have an Easter egg hunt.
Ask a grown-up to hide some
Easter eggs in the garden.
How many did you find?

. . . .

In spring the days
get warmer and there are
more hours of daylight. This
tells the plants to start
growing so they leap into
action, quickly sending out
flowers and leaves.

17

Mud Glorious Mud

There are three different types of soil: sand, clay, and silt.

Sand

Clay

Silt

1. Sandy Soils are gritty and sandy, like on a beach

2. Clay Soils are soft and squidgy, like potter's clay

3. Silty Soils are silky to the touch, like a silk tie or shirt

Most gardens have soil that is a mixture of these three things. Soils that are called **loamy** are a perfect mixture of sand, clay, and silt. Plants love loamy soils!

What sort of soil do you have?
Squidge it and roll it in your fingers.

Can you roll it into a sausage? (tick box for clay)
Does it fall to pieces? (tick box for sand)
Does it feel silky? (tick box for silt)
Does it form a loose ball? (tick box for loam)

Sand ☐
Clay ☐
Silt ☐
Loam ☐

Don't worry if you tick more than one box – your soil might be a mixture. For example, you might have a sandy loam soil.

What colour is your soil? Put a muddy thumb print here to remind you!

Spring

Lots of things live in the soil. Fill a small bucket with earth, tip it onto a piece of newspaper, and see how many creatures you can find.

Can you draw some of them?

Did you find any worms? Worms burrow through the soil and it passes through their bodies, which mixes it up and makes it better for plants.

Worms like some sorts of weather better than others. On a dry day, mark out two patches of soil. Thoroughly water one patch and leave the other dry. An hour later, fill up a small bucket with soil from each of the two sites and count the number of worms. For each worm you find, fill in a square on one of the 'wormometers' below:

WET SOIL: 🌡️

DRY SOIL: 🌡️

Number of worms

Which patch of soil had the most worms in it?

Do you think worms prefer wet or dry soil? Why?

. . . .

. . . .

> DID YOU KNOW in very dry weather worms curl and knot themselves into a tight ball and become dormant to conserve water. This is called aestivation.

Fact: When animals poo into the earth, it rots down and makes the soil very nutritious. Plants love it!

Basic Bird spotting

How bird-friendly is your garden? See how many of these birds you can spot.

Bluetits help in the garden by picking insect pests off plants. They nest in little holes, and their chicks hatch when there are lots and lots of juicy green caterpillars to eat.

Bluetit

Robin

Robins are a common sight in the garden. They eat worms and insects, or crumbs and seeds from the bird table. If you are gardening they will often sit boldly on a spade or twig nearby and wait for you to turn up something nice to eat.

Blackbirds eat mostly worms and insects, but they will eat crumbs and raisins if you put them out. They land and will run across the ground, grab a beakful of food, then run away again. The female, which is brown, not black, makes an untidy nest in hedges and bushes.

Blackbird

Chaffinch

Chaffinches are smart little birds and mostly eat seeds and insects. They build neat little cup-shaped nests out of moss, grass, and feathers bound with spiders' webs. The nests are lined with feathers and wool before the eggs are laid.

Goldfinches are seed eaters and can be seen swinging from teasels and thistle heads, searching for food. Pretty and striking, they were kept as pets in Victorian times, when children were paid to catch them.

Goldfinch

Draw your favourite bird

What does it eat?

Where does it nest?

CAUTION!
nesting birds
– do not
disturb!

Make a chart of the different birds you can see in your garden by colouring in a box on the chart below each time you see one.

NUMBER OF BIRDS

12
11
10
9
8
7
6
5
4
3
2
1

Blackbird | Robin | Blue-tit | Chaffinch | Goldfinch

TYPE OF BIRD

Birds need seeds and insects to eat and places to nest, so don't tidy up too much in the garden!

Birds also need water to drink and wash in so that their feathers stay fluffy and warm.

Fact: Bluetits can lay as many as 12 eggs in a single nest.

Talking to Plants

Gardening has its own language! All plants have a Latin name, so it doesn't matter which language you speak. Everyone uses Latin!

DID YOU KNOW Latin was spoken by the Romans 2000 years ago?

This is very useful, because some plants are known by different names in different parts of the world. For example, the kiwi fruit is also known as the Chinese gooseberry, and some people call them hairy pears! There is also a New Zealand bird called a kiwi, which makes things really confusing. But there is only one latin name, and that is *Actinidia deliciosa*. Can you work out what 'deliciosa' means?

The science of plant naming is called taxonomy. Each Latin name has two parts: the first part tells you what plant family it belongs to (a bit like a surname) and the second often tells you something about it - what colour it is, what it looks like, or who found it. This two-name system was invented by a Swedish man called Carolus Linnaeus.

'**lutea**' means that it is yellow; '**rubra**' = red, '**alba**' = white
'**chinensis**' tells you that it was found in China
'**arborea**' says it looks like a tree (an arboretum is a tree garden)
'**smithsonii**' tells you that it was discovered by Mr Smith!
'**grandiflora**' means 'big flower'; and '**odorata**' means 'smelly'

This the silver birch, *Betula pendula.* 'Pendula' means 'hanging' or 'dangly', referring to the droopy branch tips.

The tulip tree is called *Liriodendron tulipifera*, because its flowers look like tulips, although the plants are not related.

The purple cone-flower is aptly named *Echinacea purpurea*, after its purple daisy flowers.

This plant is called *Oxalis versicolor*. 'Versicolor' means 'to change from one colour to another'. Here, you can see them turning from red to white as they open. They look like ice creams!

The star magnolia is called *Magnolia stellata* in Latin. 'Stellata' means 'star-like'.

Can you guess which explorer *Fuchsia magellanica* is named after?

Before Linnaeus came along with his two-name system, plants were often just named according to how they looked, so you would get great long names like "**Ranunculus oppositifolium foetidus alba**". This might mean a smelly buttercup with opposite-facing leaves and white flowers. Sometimes this could get a bit silly.

Draw a plant that you have discovered and give it a Latin name. You could call it after yourself or the place where you live. What does it smell like? Is it poisonous? How big is it?

The naming of plants is a difficult matter, it isn't just one of your holiday games. At first you might think I'm as mad as a hatter, when I tell you a plant can have three different names!

name: . . . .
discovered by: . . . .

23

Visit HARLOW CARR Garden

Harlow Carr is in North Yorkshire and is colder than the other RHS gardens. It shows people what will grow in northern England.

In spring, you will find the alpine houses full of flowers, blossom on the trees, and thousands of spring bulbs across the whole garden.

'Carr' is an old English word that means 'land reclaimed from bog'. The long stream and numerous ponds are all that remains of the bog. Beyond the stream is a large wood – home of the Log-Ness Monster!

If you cannot get to Harlow Carr, you can still complete these activities – see page 110 for a list of gardens to visit in your area.

Spring's up at the Streamside!

The soil at the edge of a stream is almost always damp and boggy. This means that the plants that grow here must like lots of water. In spring, you will see some remarkable things emerging from the wet soil. Can you find the plants in the pictures? What are their latin names?

Some people call this the **umbrella plant** – can you think why? You might not see any leaves as they grow after the flowers have finished.

Latin name . . . .

Date seen . . . .

A common name for this plant is the **skunk cabbage** because the flowers smell nasty. Try and have a whiff, but be careful not to fall in the water! Like the plant above, the leaves come after the flowers, and they are huge.

Latin name . . . .

Date seen . . . .

Spring

This plant probably has the largest leaves you will ever see. It is called the **giant rhubarb** and is a monster. For big gardens only! PS, you can't eat this rhubarb.

Latin name . . . .

Date seen . . . .

The Harlow Carr stream is famous for its **candelabra primulas**. As spring turns into summer, you will see a magical display of pink, purple, and yellow flowers. This picture shows what it looks like.

The Log-Ness Monster

You will find some amazing things if you explore the Harlow Carr woods. Not every wood has a monster in it, but this one does! **Can you find him?** You will also find the remains of the front of a large building (called the folly) and lots of other strange ornaments. What other mysterious things can you find?

The monster isn't actually a monster. He's made of logs, cut from fallen trees. You will find piles of dead wood in any woodland, but this one is special because the logs are arranged in an interesting way.

Log piles make excellent homes for all sorts of plants and animals, particularly fungi and insects. Have a look at a rotting log. What sort of things do you find living or growing on or under it? **Can you find any of the following?** Tick the boxes to show which ones.

Woodlice ☐   Beetles ☐   Fungus ☐   Others
. . . .
Centipedes ☐   Worms ☐   Moss ☐
. . . .

Get a grown-up to help you make a log pile monster at home. You can use chicken wire to hold the monster together.

Explore the Woods in Spring

A deciduous wood in springtime is a wonderful place. Bright clear sunlight shines through newly opened leaves and onto fresh spring flowers. Everything is vibrant and the colours look clean and alive.

Bluebells can only be seen in the spring. They get their entire life cycle in early while it is still light enough. Soon the canopy of leaves will grow and the floor of the woods will look quite different, covered in plants that like shade instead.

Wildflower spotter

There are several different spring flowers you might see – **how many of these can you find?**

Bluebell

Date Found . . . .

Celandine

Date Found . . . .

Foxglove

Date Found . . . .

Wood Anemone

Date Found . . . .

If you find any of them growing together, then draw a line between them to link them.

Violet

Date Found . . . .

Explore tree bark

Choose a tree you like. Touch its bark with your hands and stroke it with your fingertips. Draw a ring round any of the words in this box that describe how it feels and then add a few more of your own.

rough   bobbly
     corrugated
shiny   lumpy
         hard

· · · · · ·   · · · · · ·
· · · · · ·   · · · · · ·

Trim your bark rubbing to size and stick it in here.

Make a bark rubbing by putting a piece of paper up against the bark and rub it with a soft pencil or crayon.

What does the pattern remind you of? . . . .
. . . .

Use your senses

Close your eyes and listen carefully. What can you hear?

. . . .

What do the woods smell like? . . . .

What colours can you see?. . . . .

Spring flowers can inspire poetry:

I wander'd lonely as a cloud
That floats on high o'er vales and hills,
When all at once I saw a crowd,
A host of golden daffodils,
Beside the lake, beneath the trees,
Fluttering and dancing in the breeze.

William Wordsworth

Look at the flowers around you. Can you write a poem about how they make you feel?

MY SPRING POEM

Spring Quiz

This is a fun quiz to test your knowledge of the garden in spring. Some questions are easy, some are hard, and some are up to you! You will find most of the answers at the back of the book.

1. Draw your favourite spring flower

Can you name the different parts of the flower? (See page 40 for some help).

Draw lines to show the petals, sepals, anthers, stamens and stigma. (If it is a daisy flower, see page 59.)

Write the name of the plant underneath. Does it have a latin name too?

2. Name three things that plants need to grow

Fill in the blanks. See page 12 for help.

(a) Plants get . . . . from the rain. It stops the plant wilting and it is used to make food.

(b) Energy from the. . . . . is used by plants to make food and grow bigger.

(c) The roots of plants are found in the . . . . This contains lots of nutrients and essential minerals.

> With all the things it needs to grow, a happy plant is a flowering plant!

Spring

28

3. The worms you usually get in compost bins are called brandlings or tiger worms

Why do you think this is?

. . . .

4. How good is your Latin?

See page 22 for help.

(a) Where do you think *Camellia japonica* was first found?

. . . .

(b) What colour is *Sternbergia lutea?*

. . . .

(c) What do you suppose *odoratus* means when it is used as a plant name?

. . . .

(d) What are so special about the flowers of *Magnolia grandiflora?*

. . . .

5. Frogs and toads help by eating pests in the garden

Draw a slimy treat for this frog to eat.

6. How many plants have you planted this spring?

Make a list of them here and write down their latin names.

7. Can you finish this limerick?

Use your imagination to fill in the blanks below. Anything goes!

There was an old RHS chap

Who pointed to . . . . on a map

He said . . . .

And . . . .

And flew back with his plants on his lap.

Sign your name: . . . .

8. At this time of year, you may suffer from hayfever

(a) Do you know what part of the plant causes hayfever?

. . . .

(b) Why do you think hayfever is more of a problem in spring than in winter?

. . . .

. . . .

My Spring Garden

Use things you have discovered about plants from this spring chapter to draw in your very own springtime garden. Perhaps the tree has some flowers, or bright green fresh leaves? Is there a lawn? Can you make a path for people to walk on? Are there any animals or birds in your garden?

Rose

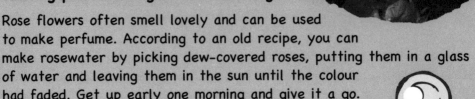

Rosa

Roses are beautiful flowers that have been grown in gardens for hundreds of years. They come in all sizes from tiny bushes of miniature flowers to enormous climbing plants that grow over 10m high.

Rose flowers often smell lovely and can be used to make perfume. According to an old recipe, you can make rosewater by picking dew-covered roses, putting them in a glass of water and leaving them in the sun until the colour had faded. Get up early one morning and give it a go.

Describe the smell here:

. . . .

. . . .

What colour is the rosewater?

. . . .

Give the perfume a name, by writing on the label here.

Wild roses have simple pale pink or white flowers and scramble into trees and hedges, hooking themselves on with sharp, curved thorns. **Garden roses** have been carefully bred to have all sorts of different colours and shapes. Some have thorns, and some have none at all.

What sort of roses grow in your garden?

Draw one of them here:

or stick in a photo.

Hawthorn trees, apples, and blackberries are all in the same family of plants as roses: Rosaceae

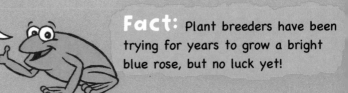

Fact: Plant breeders have been trying for years to grow a bright blue rose, but no luck yet!

Oak

Quercus

English oak trees are fairly slow growing and can live for hundreds of years. In the British Isles there are three main sorts, sessile oak, pedunculate oak and Turkey oak. One of these is not native to our country – can you tell which?

These trees lose their leaves in winter, but there is an evergreen oak called the holly or holm oak. It looks a bit like a holly tree but you can tell it is an oak because it has got acorns.

Acorns are oak seeds, and they sit in little cups. They are an important wildlife food – squirrels, birds, and mice love them!

Many different animals and insects depend on oak trees for food and somewhere to live. If you can find an oak tree, take a large sheet and spread it out on the ground underneath. Give one of the branches a good shake and then see what has fallen out. You might find moths, spiders, cater-pillars, beetles, and lots of other things as well. Make a list of what you find using this table:

Name of creature	Number found
spiders	
moths	
spiders	
caterpillars	
beetles	
. . . .	
. . . .	
. . . .	

There are hundreds of different species of oak trees that come from all over the world. Can you grow one from an acorn?

Fact: Hundreds of years ago, most of our oak trees were used to build ships. This meant that we could have a very powerful navy, and it travelled all over the world to expand the British Empire.

Currants and Gooseberries

Ribes

The gooseberry is quite easy to grow and will produce fruit even if not treated very well, but people often forget it exists – except to pretend that babies are found under gooseberry bushes.

Some gooseberries are quite sweet and can be eaten straight off the bush. Others are sour and need cooking with sugar, but make good jam. They are in the same family as black-, red-, and white-currants, but they all taste very different. See if you can find one of each to do the taste test below:

CAUTION! Ask a grown-up to help you find the fruit

Name of fruit	Where did I find it?	Rating out of 5
Whitecurrant		
Redcurrant		
Blackcurrant		
Gooseberry		

Which one did you like best?

Mum said that currants and gooseberries can grow in shade, so Daddy helped Sam and I plant some in the corner of our garden. You should do it, too – it is fun watching them grow!

Plant a currant or gooseberry bush and take a photo of yourself standing next to it. Stick the picture in here.

FACT: It is said that 95% of all Britain's blackcurrants are used to make Ribena! See **www.ribena.co.uk** to find out what happens to the other 5%.

Tomato

Lycopersicon

Tomatoes originally came from Peru in South America and were brought to Europe by the Spanish conquerors. They were golden in colour and were first known as golden apples, which is where *pomodoro*, the Italian word for tomato, comes from. They were also known as "wolf-peaches", which translates into the latin name "Lyco-persicon".

Tomatoes are actually a fruit, not a vegetable and can vary in size from tiny cherry tomatoes to giant 'beefsteak' types. They are easy to grow in pots and some bush varieties will grow in hanging baskets.

Grow a tomato in a large pot in a warm sunny place, and keep it well fed and watered. When the fruit ripens, weigh each one after you pick it and record the weights below (in grams):

When there are no more tomatoes left add up all the numbers.

How many kilograms of tomatoes did it grow? (TIP: There are 1000 grams to 1 kilogram)

Fact: All parts of tomato plants are poisonous – except the fruit. Don't eat the leaves!

2250 2500 2750
1750 2000 3000 3250
1500 3500
1250 3750
1000 4000
750 4250
500 4500
250g 4750
0kg 5kg

Mark a red line on the scale above. On average, a tomato plant will grow about 2kg of fruit during one season.

Tomatoes are hungry plants and will need feeding every week in summer with tomato fertiliser, which has plenty of potassium (or 'potash') in it for lots and lots of fruit.

35

Sunflower

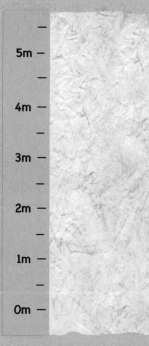

Helianthus

Sunflowers are good fun to grow! They sprout quickly and rocket up out of the ground, towering overhead like the world's biggest daisies.

There are lots of different ones to try: giants, furry-looking teddy bear types, dark red sunflowers, and ones with several flowers growing on one stem.

Grow some sunflowers against a fence or wall. When they are all flowering get an adult to take a picture of you standing next to them and stick it in here.

FACT:
Sunflower seeds are tasty to eat. **Try a few!** Birds love them.

Measure your biggest sunflower.
How tall is it?

Draw a picture of it against the height chart below:

```
—
5m —
—
4m —
—
3m —
—
2m —
—
1m —
—
0m —
```

Look out that slugs and snails don't eat your sunflowers when they are young!

Jerusalem artichokes are a type of sunflower. They are called this not because they come from Jerusalem, but because Jerusalem sounds like *'gira sole'* –the Italian for 'following the sun'.
Try this:
On a sunny day, note which way a sunflower is facing at about 10am. Take another look at 1pm and 4pm. What do you notice?

Poppy

Papaver

Wild poppies are pretty plants that used to be very common in cornfields. But farming has become more intensive and farmers have got better at keeping out plants they don't want. This means that poppies and lots of other wild flowers have got much rarer.

Poppy seeds need a burst of light to germinate. They can lie asleep in the ground for many years, and when the earth is disturbed and the light hits them they spring into life. This explains why you often get poppies on the edge of roads where there have been roadworks.

When you go on a car or train journey, count the number of patches of poppies you see. How many did you see? . . . .

During the First World War, nearly 100 years ago, the battleground became very churned up from all of the fighting. When the war stopped, the ground became covered with a blanket of blood-red poppies. Nowadays, people wear poppies to remember soldiers who died in war.

Can you think of another flower or plant that is used as a symbol or emblem? . . . .

What does it symbolise? . . . .

Poppy seed pods are like pepperpots. When they are dry, pick one, turn it upsidedown and give it a shake. Collect all the seeds that fall out.

Sprinkle them on a bare patch of earth and water them in.

See what happens!

FACT: Poppy seeds are used in cooking. Sometimes you see them sprinkled on cakes or buns.

> Poppies are annuals, which mean they grow, flower, and die all in the same year.

Good and Bad Bugs

The garden is full of villainous plant-eating pests, but fortunately in the constant battle between good and evil there are also superhero bugs that are on the gardener's side.

The Garden Villains

LILY BEETLE

VINE WEEVIL AND GRUBS

SLUGS AND SNAILS

WANTED

for chewing holes in lilies and fritillaries and having horrid larvae. This beetle arrived in the UK in 1940 and is marching steadily northwards, devastating flowers as it goes.

WANTED

for preying on innocent container plants. Vine Weevil Senior likes to bite deep notches in leaves, while her C-shaped grub is busy underground eating roots: a terrible crime!

WANTED

for hiding out under stones and in damp corners. This devilish bunch have rasping mouthparts that make short work of leaves and seedlings.

The Garden Superheroes

LADY BIRD

"THE LACEWING"

GROUNDBEETLE

Smart and dashing, Lady Bird and her larvae wage a ferocious war on greenfly and blackfly.

Don't be fooled by appearances, her larvae love to eat aphids for lunch.

Like Batman, he works by night, making short work slimy slug villains.

There are 46 species of ladybird in the British isles. They are big and small, can be yellow, red or black and have different numbers of spots. How many can you find? Colour the different types you find here:

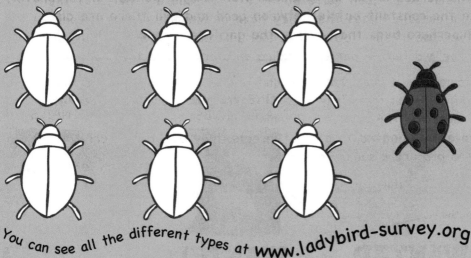

You can see all the different types at www.ladybird-survey.org

Why not go on a bug safari and see what sorts of insects you can find? Describe your favourite here:

There are loads of other exciting creepy crawlies. **Maybugs,** or cockchafers, are big fat brown beetles with feathery antennae. They fly at night and sometimes bump into lights or windows. Look out for maybugs that have knocked themselves out!

Grasshoppers 'sing' to each other. Short-horned grasshoppers sing by rubbing their back legs together and have their ears in their knees, while long-horned grasshoppers rub their wings together and have their ears on their tummies! And yes, they do eat grass.

Dung beetles collect balls of animal poo and lay their eggs in it. When they hatch, the larvae eat it all up. Yummy!

What colour is it? . . . .
How many legs does it have? . . . .
What shape is it? . . . .
How long are its feelers or antennae? . . . .
How big are its eyes? . . . .
Were did you find it? . . . .
. . . .
Why do you like it? . . . .
. . . .
What is its name? . . . .
. . . .

Play the ladybird game at www.naturedetectives.org.uk /play/games/spotted.

Looking at Flowers

Most flowers look quite different from one another, but there are certain things that they have in common: a stalk, sepals at the base of the flower (they look like green petals), petals, and male and female parts, including an ovary where the seeds grow.

Sometimes a plant has male and female parts on separate flowers, like on hazel trees (see page 8). These plants are **wind pollinated.** Plants that have male and female parts in the same flower are often **insect pollinated** to attract insects, they may be colourful, smelly, and produce a sugary nectar.

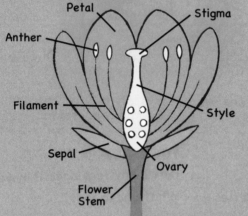

Petal

Anther

Filament

Sepal

Stigma

Style

Ovary

Flower Stem

Here is a space for you to draw your own flower.

This drawing of a flower has some labels attached to show you what the different parts are called.

Why not find a flower in the garden and copy how it looks? What do you think the labels should say? Where did you find the flower?

Many famous artists have found flowers inspiring.
Vincent van Gogh painted sunflowers, Georgia O'Keefe painted a poppy, and Claude Monet painted waterlilies and irises.

Look in the library or on the internet for their paintings, or other famous paintings of flowers. Stick a copy in here!

Quadrats

Scientists like to measure things! To count how many plants of a certain type are growing in a particular area, they use a square like the one in the picture below, which is known as a quadrat. Make one of your own out of an old metal coathanger.

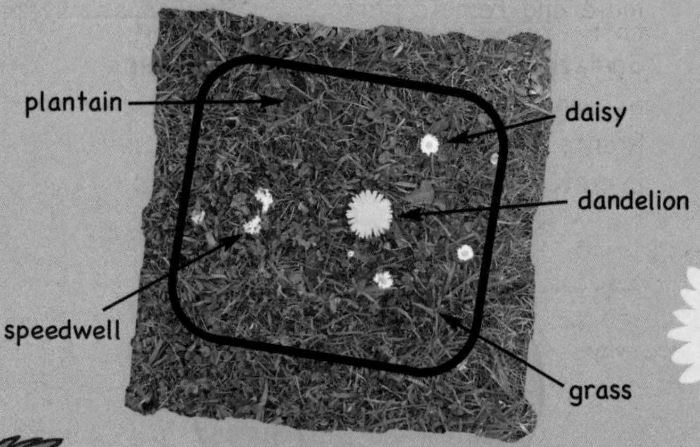

Flowers need to get pollinated so that they can make seeds, which will grow into new plants of the same sort.

plantain —

daisy

— dandelion

speedwell

grass

TYPE OF PLANT	HOW MANY IN THE SQUARE

Sign your name here:

You are a professor of botany and the University of Wisley wants to know about plants near where you live. Mark out a square quadrat anywhere in the garden, or in your local park or churchyard. What plants are in the square? How many are there of each? Fill in the table.

Some flowers have ultra-violet markings that only insects can see. They act as 'arrows' to show them where the nectar is.

Bee Fact: Botanists at Cambridge University say white musk mallow is the bumble bee's favourite flower. Why don't you plant some in your garden?

Butterflies and Moths

Butterfly

Many flowers need butterflies and moths to help with pollination, and butterflies and moths need flowers for food.

Moth
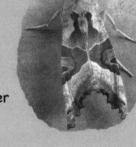

When a butterfly is not eating, its proboscis is tightly curled up out of the way.

Butterflies and moths have special mouthparts called a **proboscis,** which is a long tube like a flexible straw. This reaches right down inside the flower to get to the sugary nectar. As they do this, pollen sticks to hairs on their bodies and it is spread to the next flower they visit. The nectar is their reward.

Can you tell the difference between a butterfly and a moth?

- Moths mostly fly at night. Butterflies prefer the day.
- When resting, moths lay their wings flat. Butterflies fold their wings together above their bodies.
- Butterfly antennae always have a knob at the end. Moth antennae can be all sorts of different shapes: feathery, comb-like, or bristly.
- Moths have fuzzy bodies. Butterflies have smooth bodies.
- Butterflies are usually much more brightly coloured than moths.

Where do they come from?

Butterflies and moths lay little eggs underneath leaves. These hatch into tiny caterpillars that eat and grow until they are ready to become adults. They then form a pupa in the soil or on the plant. When the adult emerges, they will have transformed into a beautiful butterfly or moth with wings.

Which flowers are on the menu?

Butterflies and moths won't visit or eat just any old flower! They are very fussy eaters and each butterfly has special flowers for nectar and special plants for feeding their caterpillars.

Top butterfly plants include:

Buddleja, lavender, ragged robin, ice plant, thyme, Michaelmas daisy, honeysuckle, and tobacco plant.

Top caterpillar plants include:

Stinging nettle, thistle, wild carrot, bird's foot trefoil, buckthorn and blackthorn.

You can find lots more information at www.ukbutterflies.co.uk /foodplants.php

Don't get cross if caterpillars eat your plants; if there were no caterpillars, there would be no butterflies!

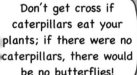

Why don't you make a butterfly garden with some of these plants?

Some butterflies and moths survive the winter by hibernating in places where they are well sheltered from wind, frost, and rain. They prefer evergreen plants, thick tangles of leaves and stems, and even garden sheds! Some species overwinter as eggs that are laid in the autumn.

Fact: If a human baby grew as fast as some species of caterpillars, it would weigh 8 tons when it was only two weeks old!

Lollipops and Other Garden Treats

In summer time there are lots of lovely things to eat in the garden. You can nibble on fruit, vegetables, herbs, and even some flowers.

How to make berry-pops

> Make sure you check with a grown up before eating anything from the garden. Some plants are poisonous.

You will need:
- Some flat lemonade. (Fruit juice or diluted squash will also do.)
- Plastic cups
- Lollipop sticks
- Sticky tape
- Fresh or frozen fruit and berries – try currants, raspberries, strawberries, blueberries, grapes, or blackberries

CAUTION!
Ask a grown-up to help you

1. Shake the lemonade to make sure it is flat.
2. Put a handful of berries into each cup.
3. Open the top of the lemonade bottle carefully to let any gas escape. Pour lemonade into each cup until it is about three-quarters full.
4. Cut a slit in a piece of sticky tape, stick over the top of the cup, and poke a lollipop stick though the hole to fix it upright.
5. Freeze for at least four hours or until it is solid.
6. When you are ready to eat your berry-pop, take it out of the freezer, remove the sticky tape and plastic cup, and enjoy.

Take a picture of yourself with your berry-pop, and stick it in here!

Summer

Fantastic floral ice cubes

Some flowers are edible and can be eaten in salads or used to decorate summer drinks.

You can eat:

Chive, nasturtium, rose, lavender, borage, calendula, and violet.

You will need:
- An ice cube tray
- Water
- Flowers or petals from the list below – small flowers like borage and violets will work best

Why not use stems of lavender as swizzle sticks?

1. Pop a few flowers or petals into each compartment of the ice cube tray.
2. Fill up with water and freeze for at least four hours.
3. Drop into a glass or jug of water or lemonade and enjoy!

Vegetable kebabs

If you are having a barbecue why not try making mini veg kebabs?

1. Soak the cocktail sticks or skewers in water before you start, then thread your veg onto them like a string of beads.
2. Make a marinade by mixing together some olive oil and a splash of lemon juice or balsamic vinegar. Add a clove of finely chopped garlic if you like it.
3. Cover your kebab in marinade by dipping it into a dish or brushing it over.
4. Get a grown up to put your kebab on the barbecue for a few minutes, turning occasionally until it starts to go brown.

You will need:
- Cocktail sticks or small wooden skewers
- Onions cut into chunks or spring onions with the green bit cut off
- Cherry tomatoes
- Courgette chunks
- Button mushrooms
- Red, green and yellow peppers, cut into chunks

CAUTION!
Ask a grown-up to help you

For the marinade
- Olive oil
- Balsamic vinegar or lemon juice
- Garlic, but only if you like it!

Colour Magic

Plants are all sort of colours because they contain various pigments and chemicals mixed together, a bit like paint colours. You can separate these colours out using chromatography.

Beetroot is purple,
woad it is blue,
I'm mashing red cabbage
and blackberries too!

You will need:
- Some blotting paper (available from a good stationery shop) cut into a strip about 10cm long and 2cm wide.
- A brightly coloured piece of plant – a leaf, some berries or piece of root. Try red cabbage, raspberry juice, or red, blue or purple flowers.
- A pencil
- A tall glass and some water
- Sticky tape   • Ruler
- A grater or masher

1. Draw a pencil line on your piece of blotting paper about a quarter of the way up.

2. Mash or grate your plant so you get some juice, you need to break up the plant to get the colour out.

3. Blob a little bit of juice onto the pencil line on the blotting paper.

4. Attach the top of the paper to the pencil using a piece of sticky tape and balance it across the top of the glass, as shown

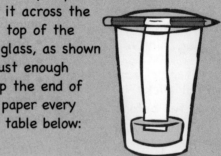

here. There should be just enough water in the glass to dip the end of the paper in. Check the paper every 15–30 mins and fill in the table below:

TIME	NO. OF COLOURS VISIBLE	HOW FAR THE WATER HAS MOVED UP THE PAPER
2 HOURS		
1 hr 45 m		
1 hr 30 m		
1 hr 15 m		
1 HOUR		
45 mins		
30 mins		
15 mins		

After the experiment is over, dry your paper and stick it here: ↗

Dyes

In the past all cloth was the natural colour of cotton or wool – various shades of brown and grey – and pretty much the only way to brighten up your wardrobe was to dye fabric with plant juices.

This involves making a kind of soup by boiling or mashing plant material with water and then leaving the cloth to soak. Sometimes other chemicals like alum (potassium aluminium sulphate) were added to 'fix' the colour permanently and stop it washing out.

CAUTION! Ask a grown-up to help you

TRY THIS:

1. Get a small piece of old, white cotton sheet.
2. Make a 'tea' by boiling onion skins in water, add the sheet and leave it to soak overnight.
3. How does it look? Do you get different colours if you use other plants like red onion, red cabbage, lichen, blackberry, walnut leaves and coffee? Fill in the chart below:

PLANT	COLOUR

Henna is an orangey dye, from the leaves of a desert tree. People use it to dye their hair or make temporary 'tattoos' or patterns on their skin.

Fact: One of the oldest blue dyes is a form of indigo called woad. It has been used since Neolithic times.

Mash up some brightly coloured leaves, berries, veg, and petals to make 'paint'. You could try blackberries, grass, rose petals, grated carrot, or beetroot.

Paint a picture here:

What did you use?

. . . .
. . . .

Visit the Dry Garden at HYDE HALL

The RHS Garden at Hyde Hall in Essex is located in one of the driest areas of the UK. There is much less rain here than in the other RHS gardens.

One of the aims of the garden is to show that even though it might only get a little bit of rain, it is still possible to grow a garden full of beautiful plants.

Hyde Hall Garden is full of amazing plants, and if you look closely at some of them, you will see clever features that help the plants cope with their dry environment.

If you cannot get to Hyde Hall, you can still complete these activities – see page 110 to get ideas of gardens to visit.

Plants that can beat the drought

Have you ever heard grown-ups complaining about not being allowed to water the garden? Maybe when it is really hot and dry in the summer, or if there is a hosepipe ban?

You don't actually need to water the lawn! And lots of plants survive without watering. **See if you can find some of these:**

Leaves that are grey or silvery, sometimes with a greenish or blue colour, reflect a lot of light to keep the plant cool in the hot sun. Often, the leaves will also be thick and leathery, which keeps moisture locked inside.

Can you find this plant? Write its name here:

. . . .

Thick, juicy, or leathery leaves can store a lot of water. Plants like this yucca are very good at this, and so are cacti.

Can you find this plant? Write its name here:

. . . .

Hairy or felty leaves trap damp air around the leaf surface, which reduces evaporation to keep water in the leaf.

Can you find this plant? Write its name here:

. . . .

One way to reduce water loss is to have almost no leaves at all! Instead, these plants have extra-small, needle-like leaves or spines.

Can you find this plant? Write its name here:

. . . .

Bulbs keep a plant safe underground when the weather gets really hot and dry. The leaves and flowers may die, but will grow back when it rains.

Can you find this plant? Write its name here:

. . . .

What lies beneath?

Most drought-tolerant plants don't like to get their roots wet. This is difficult in winter, when heavy rains make the soil quite soggy. Look at the gritty ground of the Dry Garden at Hyde Hall. When the garden was planted in 2001, a lot of old rubble and stones were dug into the soil to help rainwater drain away.

NO WET FEET!

Visit a Meadow

A meadow on a warm summer day is a lovely place, full of wild flowers and delicate grasses. It is calm and gentle, but not always quiet!

Meadows are home to lots of wildlife all jumping and buzzing and flying and singing. You get grasshoppers, different sorts of bee, butterflies, and lots of other insects, which attract birds that feed on them. In the dense 'thatch' of grass near the ground live mice-like animals called voles, as well as frogs, and slugs and snails – all hiding from the sun.

Lie on your back with your eyes shut and listen very carefully. How many different sorts of noises can you hear? What are they?

Some plants you might find in a meadow are: Can you find any of them?

Grasses
Ladies' smock
Ladies' bedstraw
Yellow rattle
Knapweed
Dock

Grasses

Grass flowers are on long stalks, which grow up into the air so that the wind will catch the pollen and blow it to another flower. You may be able to see the little flowers, which are usually yellow and covered in pollen, poking out of the case that the seed will grow in.

If you walk through tall, dry grass your clothes end up all dusty with pollen. Try turning your trousers up at the bottom; they will fill up with all sorts of seeds and bits of plant. Empty them out when you get home. What do you find? Can you grow any of the seeds? What do they turn into?

Mow patterns in your lawn and let some bits grow long to see what flowers grow. It helps the lawn stay green, and it will also attract wildlife.

Fact: The dry seedheads of yellow rattle actually do rattle! Can you find any other noisy plants?

Grasses have become popular in garden designs. They can be short and spiky, tall and wavy, or have interesting leaf colours or flowerheads.

How many different types of grass flowerheads can you find in the meadow?

Show what sorts of shape they are by drawing a few of them here:

Press some flowers!

Pressing flowers dries them out, but they still look nice and keep their colours so you can remember what they looked like fresh. It's very easy:

- Choose a suitable flower and lay it between two sheets of tissue paper.
- Sandwich the flower and tissue paper between several sheets of newspaper and put it inside a large book.
- Put several more large books on top and leave it for at least a week.

↖ **Stick one here!**

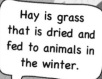

Hay is grass that is dried and fed to animals in the winter.

Small, delicate flowers press best. I used mine to make a card for father's day, and also a bookmark!

'Make a daisy chain!'

At the seaside

Life is tough at the seaside. There is not much fresh water around for plants to drink, and there is so much wind that a normal garden plant would just dry out like washing on a windy day.

There are all sorts of things to make life dry and difficult. It's windy, there is salt in the soil, sand gets blown around and hits the plants like sandpaper, and water just runs straight through sandy soil, so the roots don't have much to drink.

But seaside plants are clever. They have cunning adaptations that allow them to deal with all these problems.

The drought busters

Marram grass has an enormous root system that reaches deep into the soil to find as much water as possible. Its stems have hairs on the inside and can curl up into a tube when the weather is dry; this traps damp air and stops the plant losing water.

Hottentot fig is a South African alien that has made its home on some British sea cliffs and rocks. Its thick, juicy leaves can store lots of water.

Tiny **thrift** perches above the shore on exposed cliffs and outcrops. It has small leaves and papery flowers so that it doesn't lose too much water into the air by evaporation.

Sea holly has hard, prickly leaves to stop water evaporating and to stop rabbits from nibbling them. It is also a light greyish blue colour, which reflects light and stops it getting too hot in the sun.

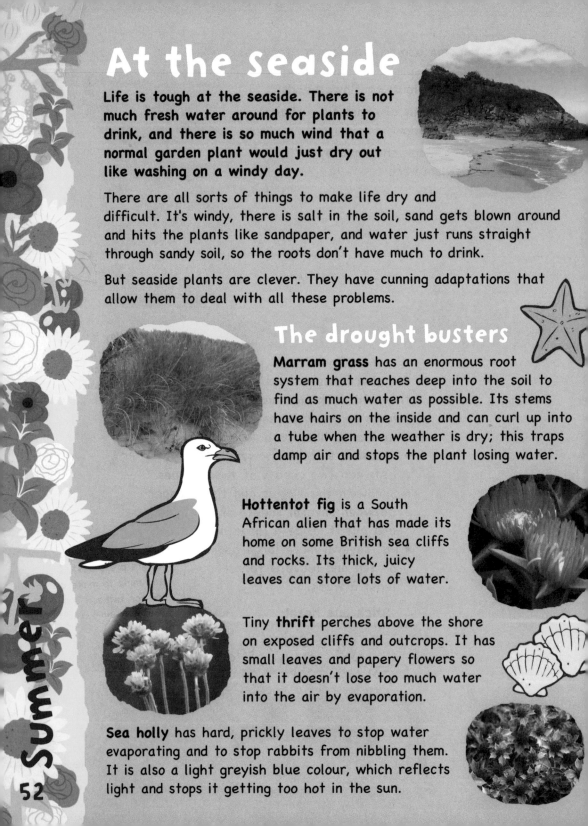

Stick your photo in here

Imagine that you are a plant hunter, exploring an exciting new coastline for the first time.
Find some plants that are pretty enough to grow in gardens and ask someone to take your photo standing next to them.
Can you give them a name?

Sand dunes

Sand dunes are delicate ecosystems and are mostly held in place by the plants that grow on them. s you walk home from the beach notice how the plants change from short, tough, stringy, leathery species at the top of the beach to a much wider variety of more delicate plants and trees further away from the sea.

The big roots of marram grass trap sand and stops sand dunes blowing away.

Plants rock!

Plants that live in difficult places are often quite small. Look at the cliffs and rocks just above the high tide mark – even the steepest has little plants hanging on by their roots in tiny cracks and making do with a bit of seagull poo for food.

When you get home look in the garden. Can you see any seaside plants?

Seaweed

Life began in the sea millions of years ago when the simplest plants appeared. These were called **algae** and were made up of just one cell – the smallest unit of life. You still get little algae made up of just a few cells living in water, but at the seaside you also get larger algae – called seaweed!

Go down to the beach at low tide. Notice how many different colours of seaweed there are. At the top of the beach there is dark green seaweed, and further down you might find bright green seaweed, the colour of lettuce. Down by the low tide mark, where the water is deep for most of the day, you will probably find red seaweed.

53

Summer Quiz

This is a fun quiz to test your knowledge of the garden in summer. Some questions are easy, some are hard, and some are up to you! You will find most of the answers at the back of the book.

1. Name three differences between butterflies and moths

1. ....
2. ....
3. ....

2. Fill in the gaps

Butterflies lay .... on plants and these hatch into

....

In summer the butterflies feed on ....
from flowers and during the winter they ....
in sheltered corners of the garden.

3. What do ladybirds eat? ....

....

4. Grass flowers are pollinated by bees

Is it **true** or **false**? ....

5. Name these three edible flowers

6. You must water your lawn to keep it alive when the weather is hot and dry

Is this **true** or **false**?

7. Finish this poem

Grasshopper is a funny bug

His ears are in his knees

....

.... breeze.

8. Plants that come from hot or dry places are specially adapted to help them find and hold onto water

Look at the box below to see the different leaves that these plants might have. **Why are they like this?**

APPEARANCE	REASON WHY THE PLANT LOOKS LIKE THIS
Grey or silver leaves:	. . . .
Thick, leathery or juicy leaves	. . . .
Hairy or 'felty' leaves	. . . .
Extra-small, needle-like leaves or spines	. . . .

9. Can you crack the code?

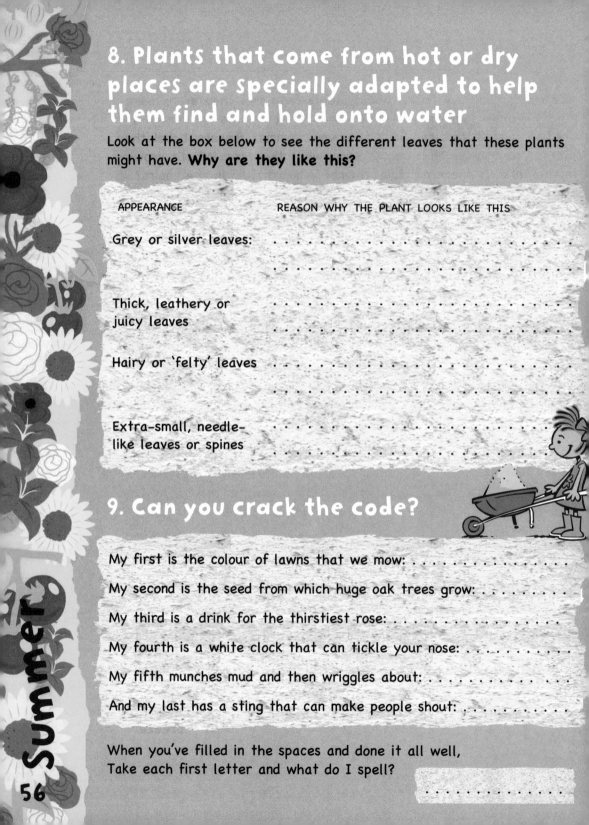

My first is the colour of lawns that we mow: . . . .

My second is the seed from which huge oak trees grow: . . . .

My third is a drink for the thirstiest rose: . . . .

My fourth is a white clock that can tickle your nose: . . . .

My fifth munches mud and then wriggles about: . . . .

And my last has a sting that can make people shout: . . . .

When you've filled in the spaces and done it all well,
Take each first letter and what do I spell?

. . . .

My Summer Garden

Use things you have learnt about plants from this chapter to make your very own summer garden. Draw in lots of plants and design a trail so that visitors can walk past your summer flowers. Label the plants you draw so that people know what they are. What's growing in the pots? Is there a colour theme? Who's sitting in the chairs?

Maple

Maple trees are known all over the world for their amazing autumn colours. In North America, the colours of maple woods are so impressive that tourists come from all over the world to see them. In Canada, sap is collected from trees in early spring to turn into maple syrup.

Fact: Maple syrup is actually made from the sap or juice of a maple tree. As the sap rises in spring, a kind of tap is put into the tree. The sap is traditionally collected in a bucket and then boiled until it is thick.

Japanese maples are very pretty and delicate small trees. The leaves have between five and nine points and some species have dainty, feathery leaf edges.

Print some maple leaves

The leaves of maple trees turn gorgeous red and yellow colours before they fall off in autumn. Choose some leaves with good shapes and spread some red, orange and yellow paint over the back of them.

Make leaf prints here:

Make a note of the tree they came from here:

Autumn Daisies

Asteraceae

Daisy plants really stand out from September onwards. Some of the biggest and most exciting come from the prairies of North America. These include echinaceas and rudbeckias.

FACT: The name Echinacea comes from the Greek 'echinos', meaning 'hedgehog'. Can you see a spiny brown dome in the middle of the flower?

Asters or Michaelmas daisies are traditional autumn flowers in British gardens. Michaelmas is the Christian festival of St Michael on 29th September. They are tall plants with white, pink, red, purple, and blue flowers – they are excellent for picking.

The name aster comes from the Greek word for star.

The daisies that are found in lawns only open up during the day and then close up again at night. This gave them their name: "Day's Eye".

What other daisies do this? Are there any that don't? Do they open on cloudy days?

Butterflies and bees love daisies, especially autumn ones, as there are fewer other flowers for them to feed on in autumn.

There are many different daisy-type flowers. **How many can you spot?**

Press your favourite daisies (see page 51) and stick them in here.

Which are your favourites?

Write their names here:

59

Walnut

Juglans

The walnut is a very useful tree. The wood makes attractive furniture and the tasty nuts are full of protein and essential Omega-3 and Omega-6 oils. The leaves can be used to a make a dye (see pages 46–47), and it even looks nice in the garden.

Walnuts can grow over 25m tall; there are some that grow smaller, but they are a bit too big for town gardens.

Squirrels absolutely love walnuts. They bury them in the ground for later and when they forget about them you get lots of little walnut trees.

The nut you see in the shops actually grows on the tree inside a green fleshy coating, like a conker.

Fact: Unripe walnuts are pickled in June or July and eaten as a delicacy with stinky Stilton cheese. They are a bit like marmite, you either love them or hate them!

The uniforms for the soldiers in the American Civil War were dyed with walnut leaves. **Create a dye or ink by mashing walnut leaves with some water and colour in this spot:**

. . . or just rub a leaf on the spot and see what happens.

Walnuts are a long-lived tree. There is a saying that you don't plant a walnut for yourself, you plant it for your grandchildren.

Plant a walnut and see if it grows. Write a note to your grandchildren here to tell them why you did it.

Autumn

60

Old Man's Beard

Clematis

The Old Man's Beard belongs to a large family of climbing, flowering plants called **clematis**. They often have pretty seedheads.

The wild variety, *Clematis vitalba*, climbs into trees and hedges. In autumn, it covers them in clouds of fluffy grey seedheads – like an old man's beard!

Can you find any Old Man's Beard?
Stick some on this old man's face and head.

What's his name?

Plants need haircuts just like people. There are different styles to choose from:

Group 1 clematis flower in late spring. Give them **a light trim** in early summer so they don't get too hot and shaggy.

Group 2 clematis have showy flowers in summer. Give them **a little tidy up** right at the start of the spring season – just enough to keep them smart and neat.

Group 3 clematis flower in late summer and autumn. They are natural skinheads – in early spring, **cut them right down to the ground.** They will grow right back – they love it!

All clematis plants need a trim if they are to grow the best flowers. This is called **pruning**. Even experienced gardeners sometimes find clematis pruning a bit scary, but all you need to remember is that there are 3 types of clematis!

FACT:
Clematis are in the buttercup family!

It's as easy as 1, 2, 3!

What sort of haircut will your old man need, above?

Apple

Malus

Orchards and apple trees are a major feature of the British countryside. They have an interesting history and are involved in many traditions. They are also valuable for wildlife. The first apples came from the mountains of central Asia, between China and Kazakhstan. Cultivated apples were brought to Britain by the Romans.

Growing apple trees from seed brings about natural variation. This is how we get new varieties of apple.

Plant some apple pips. What sort of apple pip did you plant?

....

....

What will you call your new apple?

Pruning

Apples are pruned in the winter when they are resting (see page 97). There are four main reasons why plants are pruned:

- to remove dead bits
- to control how big it gets
- to create a good shape
- to make the plant produce more fruit or flowers

Fact: Apples are propagated by cutting (see page 95). This is because they don't come true from seed: if you plant a pip from a Granny Smith apple you won't get a Granny Smith tree. You will get an entirely random sort of apple.

Make a blackberry and apple crumble

INGREDIENTS:
1/2lb blackberries
1lb apples
6oz wholemeal flour
4oz soft brown sugar
4oz butter or margarine

Ask a grown-up to help you!

You can add cinnamon or rolled oats to the topping for variety.

Blackberry

Rubus

Wild blackberries are also called brambles. It is a rampant plant with viciously thorny stems. They grow into great tangled thickets, making the fruit hard to get to.

But . . . the fruit is tasty to eat, either fresh or in crumbles and puddings. It also makes a delicious jam or clear jelly.

Because most gardeners don't want this great, wild thug about there have been new varieties grown. Some of these have been crossed with raspberries, so you still get juicy fruit, but they have much better manners!

Can you find jostaberries, boysenberries, tayberries, or loganberries in the shops? **Which is your favourite?**

There are also ornamental blackberries with ghostly white stems, such as *Rubus cockburnianus*.

The secrets of success

FACT:
Blackberries are made up of lots of little berries called drupelets.

Blackberries grow really fast. Birds love to eat the berries, and as a result, the seeds get spread all over the place in their droppings. The long, arching stems also take root very quickly. Whenever one touches the ground, it will sprout roots and grow into a new bush.

Can you find a new blackberry plant that has just taken root? Ask a grown up to help you dig it up and grow it on in a pot of soil. Be careful of the thorns!

PREPARATION:
1. Wash the blackberries; peel, core, and thickly slice the apples.
2. Rub together flour and butter, stirring in sugar, to make crumble.
3. Butter a shallow casserole dish and fill with blackberries and apples, adding a sprinkle of sugar if the apples are sour
4. Top with crumble topping and bake in oven at 180°C/350°F (Gas mark 4/5) for 30–40 minutes until the crumble topping is lightly browned and crisp, and the fruit is soft.

Spider Safari

In the autumn, garden spiders can be seen sitting in the middle of their webs, which they have strung between plants. They lay batches of eggs, which hatch out in spring.

Find a Spider

Garden spiders have lovely markings on their backs. **Draw them on this picture of a spider:**

If you can't find a real spider to copy, give it a smart pattern of your own.

Visit www.uksafari.com/spiders.htm to find out more!

Fact: There are over 600 different sorts of spider in the UK. The diving bell spider even lives under water!

The garden is full of all sorts of exciting spiders. Can you find the jumping black and white zebra spider and the wolf spider?

Go on a spider hunt. How many of each type can you find?

Spiders do not eat plants, but other animals. They are predators.

Spin a Web

Fill a plant sprayer with water and gently mist a spider's web with fine droplets so that you can see it properly. Draw it on the bushes:

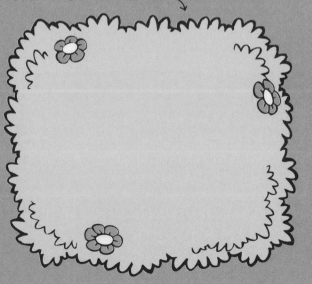

Where is the spider?

After spinning its sticky web, the spider will wait for a fly or other small bug to get trapped. The spider can feel the prey hitting the web and struggling to escape because the web lines vibrate.

Can you show the spider and what it will be having for lunch?

What spiders do for us

Spiders are very useful in the garden as they eat pests that damage plants, and also stinging insects. People often use chemical sprays to do this job, but the trouble with this is that they don't just kill the bad bugs, they kill the good bugs too, including spiders. This leaves other creatures like birds with nothing to eat.

It's much better to encourage spiders, and all the other creatures, that naturally eat up the pests. See pages 38–39.

Fact: When they hatch out, baby spiders make a long strand of spider silk that is caught by the wind like a balloon and carries them away to a new home.

Ask a grown-up to help you!

Make your Garden Spider-Friendly!

Cover bare patches of soil with a mulch. Every garden should have mulch – it keeps the soil moist, prevents weeds, and makes a home for insects. A mulch is a soil covering that can be anything from gravel to wood chippings to garden compost.

Make sure there are lots of tall plants and dense bushes where spiders can build their webs.

Don't be too tidy! When clearing up the garden in autumn, leave some dead stems and areas untouched for overwintering habitats.

Q: Where do most spiders live? A: Crawley! Ha! Ha!

Grow lots of lovely flowers that attract the insects that spiders love to eat.

Fact: Most spiders live just one or two years. Tarantulas can live up to 20 years, but you don't get these in Europe!

Make a Pumpkin Lantern

Pumpkins and squashes are part of a big family of plants called curcurbits, which also includes cucumbers and gourds.

At this time of year it is traditional to carve a lantern out of a pumpkin for Hallowe'en, which you put in the window to scare off evil spirits. It doesn't have to be a scary face, though. You could carve a house with windows, or just a funny pattern.

For the best patterns, use a variety like 'Crown Prince', which has blue skin that is a different colour to the orange flesh underneath. Or you could enhance your design with paint or food colouring.

You will need:
- A pumpkin
- Cutting tools, including a sharp knife, a potato peeler, and an apple corer
- A felt tip pen (optional)
- A strong spoon
- A bowl to put bits of pumpkin into.
- Nightlights and box of matches

CAUTION! Ask a grown-up to help you cut

FACT: Pumpkins are 90% water. You will notice your pumpkin lantern starts to shrivel as it dries out.

1. **Cut off the top of your pumpkin** to make a lid.
2. **Scoop out** all the icky, slimy seeds.
3. **Carefully scrape the pumpkin flesh** off the inside wall of the pumpkin and put it in the bowl.
   You can cook and eat this bit. Americans are very keen on pumpkin pie. Try these websites for recipes:
   www.camellia.org/kitchen/pumpkin-pie.html
   southernfood.about.com/od/pumpkinpies/r/bl21016d.htm
4. **Draw your design** onto the outside of the pumpkin with a felt tip pen.
5. **Carefully cut out the design** you have drawn with the cutting tool
6. **Light the nightlight,** carefully drop it inside, and put on the lid
7. **Turn out the lights** – watch out witches and ghosties!

Draw your pumpkin lantern in this space here, or stick in a photo:

How to grow a pumpkin

Pumpkins are quite easy to grow as long as they get plenty of food and water. You plant one seed in a little pot of compost in March or April, and in early June plant them into the ground when there will be no more frost, remembering to feed and water them regularly – use tomato fertiliser.

While they are young, just as the fruit start to turn yellow, scrape the skin with something sharp like a pencil or nail. The skin will heal but a scar will be left showing your name or pattern.

If they get too hot and dry they may get powdery mildew, which is a disease that looks like talcum powder has covered the leaves. Water your pumpkins more to fix the problem!

Fact: Pumpkin and squash flowers are edible!

67

Plant Some Bulbs for Spring

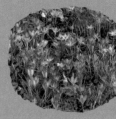

Autumn is the time of year to plant bulbs so you get flowers for spring. If you plant them in pots they can be moved to a good position when they come out. They also make lovely Christmas presents.

There are lots of different types: crocuses, dwarf irises, grape hyacinths, tulips, lots and lots of daffodils – there are hundreds!

The usual rule is to plant the bulb three times as deep as it is high, so the bigger the bulb the deeper the hole. **Plant some in pots using the steps below:**

1. Put some good compost in the bottom of a pot. Make sure your pot has holes in the bottom and is deep enough for the bulbs you are planting.

2. Place the bulbs on top of the compost. Instructions on the packet will tell you how far apart to plant them in the garden, but a good trick if you plant in a pot is to put in as many as will fit without touching. When all the flowers come out they will look amazing.

3. Fill up to the top with more compost, and firm the soil down. Water well and put it somewhere sheltered outside, where it won't get too wet or dry out completely. In late winter you will see the little green shoots poking through the soil.

4. In spring, your bulbs will come into flower. **Draw what it looks like here, or stick in a photo:**

I mixed up different types of bulbs in my pot.

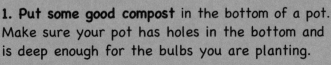

Early to bed, early to rise

Some bulbs like snowdrops and crocuses like to flower good and early in January and February. They are very hardy and don't even mind if they get snowed on! Daffodils and grape hyacinths arrive in spring as things start to warm up, and tulips are usually the last to arrive and keep going until late May.

But you get early and late daffodils, crocuses, and tulips, so even if you only plant one bulb family you can choose different varieties to spread the flowering out across many weeks.

FACT: Many of the bulbs that we now see in our gardens originate from hot countries like Turkey.

When you choose a mix of bulbs, think about when they will all flower!

Design a bed of bulbs

Bulbs come in all sorts of different colours. Early in the year they are pretty much the only cheerful thing you will see, but in April and May they look good next to other flowering plants like wallflowers, pansies, or forget-me-nots to make a design or colourful display.

On paper, design a display of bulbs for a pot or patch of the garden using your favourite colours. You can get bulbs in all colours. Then, ask a grown-up to help you buy and plant the bulbs.

You could choose colours to match your front door, your favourite football team, or the colours that you or someone you know likes to wear. Or you could choose plants that you think someone famous would like. What would the Queen plant? How would a Spiderman plant display look? How about the world's greatest pop star?

FACT: Although they look a bit like onions, some bulbs are poisonous and should never be eaten.

When the spring comes, paint or photograph how your design turns out and stick it in here:

69

Measure the Weather

Plants depend on weather. They need water and sunshine to grow, but day length and temperature matter too. When the days get warmer and longer in spring, this tells plants that have been resting over winter to start growing again.

When the days get shorter in autumn and winter, most plants know to stop growing. But for some 'short-day plants', like chrysanthemums, the change in autumn tells them to start flowering.

But weather ignores plants!

When there is not enough water, there is a drought. Most plants will die if they don't get enough water.

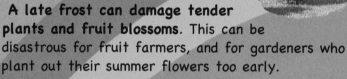

A late frost can damage tender plants and fruit blossoms. This can be disastrous for fruit farmers, and for gardeners who plant out their summer flowers too early.

If the weather is too cold or cloudy, flowers may not open and the plant will just have to wait to be pollinated.

A little bit of wind is good, as it spreads pollen and strengthens plant stems by moving them. But storms can knock over plants and tear branches off trees. Disaster!

So plants have to put up with it, unless we can sometimes help them out by watering them, moving them, snuggling them up with fleece, or by providing shelter from wind.

The best plan is to choose plants that will do well where you want to put them. Choosing plants that will be unhappy and need lots of help makes lots of extra work.

Fact: Plants need water, but too much water is bad for them. More houseplants die from overwatering than from underwatering, so keep the compost just moist to the touch!

Autumn

You can measure the weather at home, just like a meteorologist.
All you need is some simple equipment to measure the wind, air temperature, air pressure, and rainfall. Write down your records in a special note book. Check the weather at the same time each day.

Wind direction

Someone who measures and predicts the weather is called a meteorologist.

Use a weathervane or flag on top of a nearby church or building to find out from which direction the wind is blowing. You may need a compass to tell you which way is north, south, east and west. Can you make your own weathervane?

Temperature

An ordinary thermometer just measures the temperature, but a maximum-minimum thermometer has two markers: one to move up as the temperature rises, and the other to move down as the temperature falls. They then stay at the highest and lowest point.

Air pressure

A barometer measures atmospheric pressure. This is the amount that all the air around the Earth presses down on us. It does not weigh much so we don't feel it!

When atmospheric pressure is high, the weather is often good, and when it is low is it usually wet and windy.

If you do not have a barometer of your own, check the weather in your area at: www.bbc.co.uk/weather.

Rainfall

A rain gauge is a container with markings on to measure how much rain has fallen in 24 hours (one day). You can make one out of an old drink bottle – ask a grown-up for help.

Cut the top off the bottle and mark 1 cm intervals up its side, starting just above the point where the sides of the bottle become straight. Fill with water up to the first line, which will hold the bottle down. Put your rain guage somewhere in the open.

Look at Seeds

Plants produce seeds that will grow into new plants of the same sort. This is how most plants survive across generations.

It is important that the new plants grow away from their parent, so that the parent plant does not take all their food, light, and water. They also need to be far enough away that they get pollen from a plant that is not their parent, as this helps produce stronger seeds and allows for natural variation and evolution.

Seeds spread themselves in many ways. They can have wings or parachutes so they glide away in the wind, such as these sycamore seeds.

Seeds like tomatoes and strawberries may have juicy fruit around them so that they are eaten and then spread in poo, which is a handy source of fertilizer.

Seeds can have little hooks that cling onto fur or clothing as creatures and people brush past.

Some seeds can float when dropped into water, so that they drift away downstream. Others, like dandelions, are light enough just to be carried away in the breeze. Certain seeds are fired away from exploding seed pods! (See page 85).

People often have funny names for seeds, especially sticky ones!

Make a list here of names that people use for seeds. For example, horse chestnut seeds are known as conkers. Ask people you know if they know any names. Can you make up your own?

Collect some seeds

If you collect seeds in autumn you will be able to plant them when spring comes, to grow new plants of your own.

Get some small envelopes and shake seedheads into them, or rub ripe seeds off a flowerhead with your fingers. Label the envelopes with a pencil. Store them in a cool dry place, or in the fridge, and sow them when the weather warms up.

You will notice that all the seeds that you have found look different. Draw some in these spaces below (or fix them in under a piece of sticky tape). Write their name underneath so you know what they are!

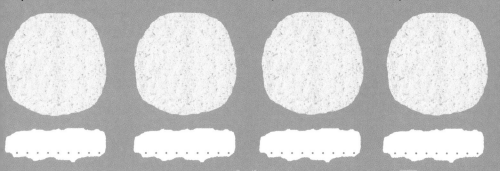

Fact: If stored in the right conditions, seeds can last hundreds of years and still be able to germinate and grow.

The Royal Botanic Garden Kew's Millenium Seed Bank Project is the world's largest conservation project. They have over one billion seeds in cold storage. You can visit the seed bank at Kew's garden at Wakehurst Place, in West Sussex.

If you want to start your own seed bank, a special Mini Seedbank is available from: www.kew.org/msbp.

Some seeds can be planted in the autumn.
These are seeds of tough plants with seedlings that can survive winter outdoors.

Try sowing poppies, foxgloves, sweet peas, peas, or broad beans now in small pots of compost. Follow the instructions on the packet. Water them well and place them outside in a sheltered spot.

> Seeds sown in autumn will come up now, survive the winter, and make bigger plants that flower sooner in spring.

73

Make Some Hibernation Places

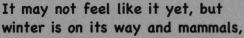

It may not feel like it yet, but winter is on its way and mammals, birds, and insects are all preparing themselves for cold weather. Many creatures hibernate, spending the winter asleep and waking up when everything warms up again in spring. Although their heart rate and breathing slow down, it still takes energy to survive and they will wake up very thin and hungry so they must eat as much food as possible before they go to sleep. **You can help by making some hibernation places in your garden.**

> If you make a home for just one creature, you will often be helping others too.

> I hide under piles of rotting logs.

Beetles

To make a place for beetles to hibernate, find an area of the garden that won't be disturbed and will stay cool, damp, and shady. Under a big bush is ideal. Get some nice big logs; it is good if they are old and rotting a bit already, but don't worry if they are freshly cut as they will rot in time. Pile up your logs into a nice big heap . . . and leave them be! It won't take long before the beasties spot the lovely home you have made and move in.

> Ask a grown-up to help you!

Fact: Stag beetle larvae can take up to 5 years to become adults, so do not disturb!

Ladybirds

Make a nice dry winter nest for ladybirds by searching the garden for old, dry plants with hollow stems. Bamboo and fennel stems are ideal. What else can you find?

Cut the stems into 10cm lengths and make a bundle, tying them together with wire or string. Hang it somewhere dry and cosy, like under the eaves of a shed.

> I hibernate in stems and under loose bark.

Autumn

Fact: Honeybees do not hibernate but spend the winter as a colony, all huddled together for warmth.

> I will tuck myself into heaps of dead leaves and twigs.

Hedgehogs

Ask an adult to make or buy a hedgehog box, which is about the size of a shoe box. Visit **www.fow.org.uk/hogbox fow.htm** to find out how to make one.

> I curl up in dry places, under piles of leaves and twigs, or under a hedge.

It needs an opening about 15cm wide in one end so that the hedge-hog can get in and out!

Fill the box with straw and put it in a quiet place that a hedgehog is likely to visit, for example under bushes or near the compost heap. Once a hedgehog is hibernating it is probably safe to have a little look, but they are best left alone to sleep. *Shhhhhhh!*

Have you ever seen a hedgehog? Describe what it was doing below:

....

....

If a grown-up is making a bonfire in your garden, it is very important to ask them to check the pile of wood, twigs, and leaves thoroughly before they set light to it. Hedgehogs may be trying to hibernate and will get hurt.

> it is important not to be too tidy in the garden, as you will remove hiding places for friendly bugs.

Fact: Hedgehogs eat slugs, snails, and other pests, so they are good to have around. They can be fed with any meat-based cat or dog food, but do not give them milk — it will make them ill.

75

Visit the Orchards at WISLEY

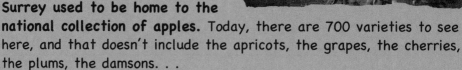

The RHS Garden at Wisley in Surrey used to be home to the national collection of apples. Today, there are 700 varieties to see here, and that doesn't include the apricots, the grapes, the cherries, the plums, the damsons. . .

If you cannot get to Wisley, see page 110 for a list of gardens to visit in your area. Some may have fruit collections.

The fruit at Wisley ripens over a long season. Strawberries are ready in early summer, and there are different types of fruit available all the way through to late autumn. Here are some apples that you might see:

'Gala' is also know as 'Royal Gala'. It was bred in New Zealand in 1934 and is widely grown there. It is a a popular sweet apple with a fresh taste.

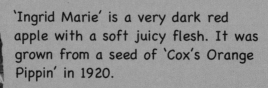

'Ingrid Marie' is a very dark red apple with a soft juicy flesh. It was grown from a seed of 'Cox's Orange Pippin' in 1920.

'Kidd's Orange Red' is another New Zealand apple, bred in 1924. It is sweet and tasty. It's parents are 'Cox's Orange Pippin' and 'Golden Delicious'.

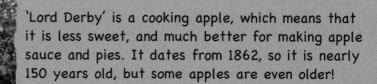

'Lord Derby' is a cooking apple, which means that it is less sweet, and much better for making apple sauce and pies. It dates from 1862, so it is nearly 150 years old, but some apples are even older!

Autumn

Don't forget the pears!

Wisley has 150 different types of pear, including 25 that come from Asia. Pears are a very historic fruit. The 'Black Worcester' pear was spotted by Queen Elizabeth I on a royal tour of Whystone Farm over 400 years ago, and it has been on the Worcester coat of arms ever since.

Worcester coat of arms

Buy some strange fruit

You can buy almost any of the fruit you see at Wisley at the shop near the entrance to the garden. A lot of the fruits have amazing names: 'Blue Pearmain', 'Ellison's Orange', 'Ginger Gold', 'Horneburger Pancake', 'Strawberry Parfait', 'Turley Winesap', and 'Winter Banana', which are all apples! **The fruit in the picture is a sort of plum called 'white bullace'.** You never see it in the shops. It tastes of honey.

I wonder what those other strange fruit taste like.

Do a taste test. How many unusual types of fruit can you find? If you can't get some from Wisley, try your local farmer's market, where there may be more 'strange' varieties available.

Name: . . . . Date found: . . . .
What does it taste like? . . . .
Rating: (was it revolting, a bit yuk, ok, pretty good, or fantastic?)
. . . .

Name: . . . . Date found: . . . .
What does it taste like? . . . .
. . . .
Rating: . . . .

Name: . . . . Date found: . . . .
What does it taste like? . . . .
. . . .
Rating: . . . .

Go Mushroom hunting!

If you go for a walk at this time of year you will see lots of mushrooms and toadstools growing in the woods, hedges, fields, and even gardens.

Mushrooms and toadstools are types of fungi. They live on plants, or dead and decaying material in the soil. Instead of roots they have long mycelium strands. The mushroom bit that you can see only appears now and again, usually in autumn when the weather is cool and damp. The purpose of the mushroom is to produce spores, which are bit like tiny seeds.

Fungi are both interesting and useful. As well as the sort of fungus we call a mushroom, there are other foods made out of fungi. These include Marmite and Quorn. Fungi can also be used to make medicines like penicillin. In the garden, fungi have an important job breaking down dead plants and poo into compost and making food available for plants to grow.

> Some fungi have brilliant names: stinkhorn, shaggy inkcap, hen of the woods, death cap, destroying angel, and slippery jack.

Here are some common wild fungi:

Field mushrooms grow on the grass and look like the mushrooms you get from shops.

Bracket fungi are shelf-like fungi that grow on trees and stumps.

Fly agaric is the poisonous fairytale toadstool with a red cap and white spots. It grows under birch, pine, and spruce trees.

Honey fungus is an enemy of the gardener as it can kill trees and shrubs. Look out for its honey-coloured mushrooms and very distinctive black, shoelace-like mycelium on the plant it is living on.

Fairy ring mushrooms grow in circles on short grass.

Shaggy inkcap is a tall, narrow white mushroom that grows on grassland. Its flesh dissolves into black 'ink' after a few days.

Fact: The largest mushroom museum in Europe is in caves in the Loire Valley, France.

Fact: Some fungi, like honey fungus, damage plants. Coral spot looks like tiny orange dots and is a common problem in the garden. If you find it, it should be cut off and burnt.

Grow some mushrooms

Some people enjoy picking wild mushrooms and fungi to eat, and there are several different varieties that you can grow at home.

CAUTION!

NEVER EAT A FUNGUS OR MUSHROOM UNLESS IT HAS BEEN CAREFULLY IDENTIFIED AS AN EDIBLE SPECIES BY AN ADULT. SOME FUNGI CAN BE VERY POISONOUS INDEED.

Oyster and shiitake mushrooms grow on logs or sawdust, and white button mushrooms are easy to grow from kits. You can even grow oyster mushrooms on unused toilet rolls!

You can buy from:
www.annforfungi.co.uk
www.gardeningexpress.co.uk
www.dobies.co.uk
www.thompson-morgan.com

A good website is www.fungi4schools.org!

Make a spore print

Mushrooms produce tiny spores, a bit like seeds, which blow away on the wind. Find an old, ripe mushroom that is fully open and where the delicate gills under the cap have darkened.

Place your mushroom gill-side down on the square opposite . . . and leave it for at least a day before removing it. It should leave a pattern where the spores have fallen out of the gills.

Stick some clear tape over the pattern to fix it in place.

A fungal foray!

Organised fungal forays are fun. Many local groups organise them in the autumn, including the Wildlife Trusts (www.wildlifetrusts.org).

Find a fungal foray near to you and make a record of your finds.

Which fungus was your favourite?

Autumn Quiz

1(a) What is the common name for *Clematis vitalba*?

....

(b) Why do you think the seedheads of this plant are all light and fluffy?

....

2. Baby spiders float away to a new home using a silk balloon

Is this **true** or **false**?  ....

3. How does this seed travel away from its parent plant?

....

 How about this one?

....

4. Which of these is a poisonous mushroom?

Field mushroom   Truffle   Fly agaric

5. Plant Sudoku

This puzzle is a 4x4 grid of boxes in which you need to put a plant and the things it needs to grow. Each thing must appear once in each row, once in each column and once in each 2x2 box. If any item appears twice in the same box, row or column the plant dies and you have to start again. Draw the missing things in the spaces in the grid.

6. Why don't you grow pumpkins in winter?

. . . .

. . . .

7. You have just found the most ugly, poisonous toadstool in the world

What are you going to call it?

. . . .

. . . .

. . . .

Draw it here:

8. What spring-flowering bulbs have you planted this autumn?

Make a list in the box:

Which is your favourite?

. . . .

Why?

. . . .

. . . .

9. Apples and Clematis are in the same family

Is this **true** or **false**? . . . .

10. Can you skip with a skipping rope?

How many skips can you do to this rhyme? . . . .

Squashes bright and pumpkin tea
Scare the ghosts away, you see.
But you can make a tasty brew,
With blackberry and apple stew.
The leaves have fallen off the trees
Squashes bright and pumpkin tea.

Can you do any better?
Write a skipping rhyme
of your own here, using
things you see in
autumn. How many
skips does it have?

Autumn

My Autumn Garden

Using the things you have seen in the autumn chapter, draw an autumn garden of your own. Label the plants that are important at this time of year. Does the tree have autumn leaves?

What plants could you add to make your garden look particularly exciting at this time of year? Draw arrows on the ground to show where you will plant your spring bulbs.

Does your garden have any mushrooms in it?

Mistletoe

Mistletoe grows in dense bushes high up in trees. Its leaves grow in pairs and it has small, white berries. Mistletoe is quite fussy about where it grows and seems to prefer apple, lime, and poplar trees.

Although mistletoe makes food with its green leaves like other plants, it is a parasite, which means that it also feeds off the tree that it is growing on, without giving anything back.

> It is traditional to kiss under a sprig of mistletoe at Christmas.

Fact: Mistletoe is slow growing. Each branch only produces one pair of leaves a year.

Next time you are going somewhere by car, count how many mistletoe bushes you can spot. How many did you see? Did you see what sort of trees they were growing on?

JOURNEY FROM:	JOURNEY TO:	NUMBER OF MISTLETOE TREES SEEN
. . . .	. . . .	. . . .
. . . .	. . . .	. . . .
. . . .	. . . .	. . . .
. . . .	. . . .	. . . .

Mistletoe berries are very sticky. When a hungry bird eats the berries, the seeds stick to its beak. The bird then has to wipe them off on the next branch it comes to and the mistletoe grows a new plant there.

If there is a mistletoe in a tree near you and you can get hold of some berries, try rubbing them into a crack on the underside of an apple tree, as if you were a bird. Do this in spring when the berries are fully ripe. How sticky were they? Did the seeds grow?

> Mistle thrushes are birds that like to eat mistletoe berries. That is why they share a name.

Winter

Witch Hazel

Hamamelis

Witch hazels are small trees. They have very pretty flowers in the middle of winter. The flowers are usually little red, orange, or yellow tassels, a bit like grated cheese.

"Witch" refers to the fact that the branches are used for water divining (a mysterious way to find water underground without digging), and "hazel" is used because the leaves resemble those of the hazel tree – see page 6.

See if you can find a witch hazel tree. Ask a grown up to cut you a twig with flowers on it. Have a close look at it. How many flowers are there? Do they smell? **Draw a flower here.**

What else can you see? How many petals do the flowers have? What colour are they? Compare it with the flower on page 40. **Are they different?**

As the fruit dry and shrink in late summer, they burst with a pop to scatter the seeds far and wide. This explosive method of seed dispersal means that new plants grow up to 10m away from their parent.

Mark out a 10m line using a tape measure. You could do this in the playground or park using some colourful chalk. Do you think you could throw a tiny seed this far? How far along the line can you and your friends throw an orange pip? Who can throw it the furthest?

Fact: Some witch hazels have red flowers, but the yellowish ones are much brighter in the winter garden.

Hamamelis, means "together with fruit," because witch hazel has ripe fruit, flowers, and next year's leaf buds all on the branch at the same time.

Witch hazel leaves also go a nice colour in autumn.

85

Yew

Taxus

Yew is a fantastic evergreen plant to have in a winter garden. It either grows into a tall, bushy tree, or it is sometimes clipped into a hedge or an interesting shape. This means that there is something green to look at when everything else is cold and bare.

DANGER!
All parts of a Yew tree are poisonous!

Clipping bushes into unusual shapes is called topiary.

Fact: Evergreen plants keep their leaves all winter. The plants that lose their leaves are known as deciduous plants.

Yew trees live for a very long time, sometimes thousands of years. A lots of myths and stories are attached to them, and they are frequently found in churchyards. Does your local churchyard have one? **Visit some more churchyards and see how many you can find:**

NAME OF CHURCHYARD	NUMBER OF YEW TREES
. . . .	. . . .
. . . .	. . . .
. . . .	. . . .
. . . .	. . . .

Yew trees are often gnarled and old ones can feel quite spooky and witchy. Ancient yew forests are very spiritual places, and they have been compared to cathedrals. The one at Kingley Vale in West Sussex is famous and is very magical.

Stand quietly under a yew tree and feel its atmosphere. Is it dark or light, heavy or magical? What does it make you think of?

Make sure you wash your hands well after touching any bit of a yew tree – **they are poisonous.**

Winter

Snowdrop

Galanthus

Dainty snowdrops are one of the first flowers to poke their heads above the ground in the New Year. They are very hardy and don't mind the cold, or even if it snows on them.

Fact: Many flowers last for longer if the weather is cool.

Snowdrops grow from a bulb underground. You plant most bulbs in the autumn, but snowdrops are better planted just after they have finished flowering, in late winter or early spring. This is called planting 'in the green'.

Find a big clump of snowdrops and dig a few of them up – ask permission first, and don't let them dry out! Plant them somewhere else in the garden, and see if they come up again next year. Write down when and where you planted them here, so you don't forget.

Do not dig plants up from the wild!

You might think that all snowdrops are the same, but this is not true! If you look carefully at snowdrops from different places you will see that there are tiny differences.

The petals on the outside may be small or quite big. They may be all white or have a tiny green spot on. And they can be different shapes.

The frilly petals on the inside can be many or few. They can have lots of green on or just a small marking. And the green colour can be a dark green or almost yellow.

You could plant some in little pots to give as presents next Christmas.

Have a look for yourself and see how many different sorts you can find.

People who are very keen on snowdrops are called galanthophiles.

Fact: *Galanthus* means 'milk flower'. In Greek, the word *'gala'* means milk and *'anthus'* means flower.

Holly

Holly is a very smart bush or small tree. It has shiny, dark green leaves – often with sharp spikes – and bright red berries.

The holly tree is a symbol of Christmas. Why don't you make a Christmas card for a friend using holly in the design?

Who could you send it to?

You could use the leaves, berries, bark, or the whole tree as a theme. Add some colour and sparkle!

Lots of different varieties of holly are grown in the garden and they are not always green. Many are variegated, with yellow or white patches on their leaves.

Some hollies are boys (male), others are girls (female). Only the female hollies have berries. The berries are usually red but they can sometimes be orange or yellow or even black.

Holly and Ivy are both used as girls names.

Find out more about these hollies by filling in the table below:

NAME OF HOLLY	MALE OR FEMALE?	SPINY OR SMOOTH?
'SILVER QUEEN'	. . . .	. . . .
'DRAGON LADY'	. . . .	. . . .
'BLUE ANGEL'	. . . .	. . . .
'FEROX ARGENTEA'	. . . .	. . . .
'GOLDEN KING'	. . . .	. . . .

Holly and ivy are celebrated by this Christmas carol which shows just how wonderful winter can be.

The holly and the i-vy, When they are both full grown, Of

all the trees that are in the wood The hol-ly wears the crown: O the

Ivy

Ivy is a climbing plant that sticks onto walls and fences using tiny aerial roots all along the stems. It has triangular leaves. If it gets big enough, and gets enough light, you will sometimes get small yellowish flowers and black berries.

Ivy is very good for wildlife. The flowers feed bees, butterflies, and hoverflies, and the thick tangle of stems and leaves makes winter homes for many butterflies and other insects. The birds eat the berries too.

Hedera

CAUTION! All parts of ivy are poisonous!

Handle with care; never eat it or get the sap on your skin.

Like holly, ivies can be variegated with white or golden markings. These are very useful if you are designing a garden and need a hardy and bright plant to climb a wall.

Curly Fact: Common English ivy is called *Hedera helix* after the way it grows. When its shoots climb a branch, its stems go round and round, and up and up. This forms a spiral or 'helix'.

Plants will only twine one way around what they are climbing. This is true for ivy, runner beans and many others.

Which way does ivy twine? Clockwise or anticlockwise?

rising of the sun And the run-ning of the deer The

pla-ying of the me-rry or- gan Sweet sing-ing of the choir.

89

Christmas Decorations

There are lots of lovely Christmas decorations you can make with things from the garden. Always ask a grown up to help you when using spray paint or sharp objects. Here are some ideas:

- Spray any pretty seedheads you can find in your garden with glue then sprinkle them with glitter.

- Thread some brightly coloured beans, poppy seedheads, or honesty seed pods onto short lengths of cotton (be careful not to spike yourself on the needle).

- Pine cones come in different shapes and sizes. Collect some and spray them lightly with silver or gold paint.

Hang them from the Christmas tree with cotton or silver thread.

If any seeds fall out of seedheads or pine cones while you are making decorations you could pot them up and see if they grow! Next year you could have your own little Christmas plant in a pot.

Make some Christmas pots

Get some small terracotta pots and draw a design on them in pencil. Paint the pot with acrylic paint. When it is dry, you could use glue to add glitter or gold stars. Tie a smart Christmassy ribbon around the top of your pot or finish with a twist of tinsel.

You could plant up your pot with winter bulbs for a lovely Christmas present.

Try snowdrops (see page 87) or any of the bulbs used for forcing indoors, such as hyacinths, dwarf daffodils, crocuses, or amaryllis (see pages 68-69).

Alternatively, buy winter-flowering plants from the shops already growing and pot them up! Try poinsettias, cyclamen, or succulent plants, like Christmas cacti.

You could use winter plants like holly and ivy, or bare twigs and leaf skeletons, in your design.

Make a wreath for your front door

You will need:
- Ivy
- Other evergreens, like holly and bits of Christmas tree
- Garden wire

CAUTION!
Ask a grown-up to help you

1. Make a circle with your longest and fattest piece of ivy. Fix the end with wire so it stays the right size and wind any spare in and out around the circle. You could use bendy willow stems for the circle if your ivy is not big enough.

2. Build up the wreath by winding more and more ivy in and out. Decide which side is the front and try and make sure that most of the leaves face towards that side.

3. Thread the other evergreens into the ivy wreath and fix with wire to hold it all together.

4. Decorate your wreath with pretty trimmings. You can use all sorts of things as trimmings: try any of the suggestions above or ribbons tied in a bow,

How did it work out?
Hang your wreath on your front door and draw a picture or stick a photo here:

Q: What do you call Santa Claus' wife? A: Mary Christmas! Ha! Ha!

Feed the Birds

Different birds like to eat different things.
There are those that eat insects, some that
prefer meat, and those that like seeds or nuts.
Some birds, like town pigeons, are scavengers.
This means they will eat almost anything if they
are hungry. Large birds of prey, like sparrowhawks,
like to eat smaller birds.

You will get more birds visiting your garden if you
put out different sorts of food.

See **www.birdfood.co.uk**
for more information.

See **www.rspb.org.uk/
youth/learn/foodchain** for
games and more details.

Make birdfood cakes

You will need:
- Suet (you can buy this from a supermarket)
- Oats
- Thick, knotted string

You can add breadcrumbs, sunflower seeds, raisins
or bought bird food to your mix too, if you like.

**Ask a
grown-up
to help
you!**

1. Melt about 3 tablespoons of suet in a saucepan over a low heat
with your grown-up helper. Don't let it get too hot.

2. Stir in enough oats to make it look like thick porridge and add a
sprinkle of seeds or bird food for a treat.

3. Let it cool down, then squidge it into cakes or into balls around
the string. Leave it to cool outside or in the fridge, then put it on
the bird table or hang from a tree outside a window.

Make sure there is some water nearby. Birds need it to drink and
to bathe in, especially if the weather gets very cold. Keeping their
feathers clean and fluffy helps them stay warm on chilly winter
nights. *Brrrrrr!*

Winter

Plant a birdfood buffet

Birds like plants that have tasty seeds or fruit, and flowers that attract insects. You can make a garden of any size into a buffet for birds, with a little help from a grown-up.

Find a place in the garden that you use. If it is near to the house, and includes some bird feeders, then you can keep a regular eye on bird activity from indoors.

You will need to give the birds some cover to hide from patrolling cats. If you have a hedge, that is great, otherwise plant some small trees and shrubs. If there are any bare walls or fences, grow some ivy or other climbing plants up their sides. A source of water, even just a bird bath, attracts insects and gives the birds something to drink and a place to bathe.

Plants to grow for bird food:
- Teasels and sunflowers, which have crunchy seeds.
- Cardoons and other thistle flowers – for the finches.
- Berrying shrubs like cotoneaster, blackthorn, or pyracantha.
- Wildflowers like marigolds, buttercups, cornflowers, and oxeye daisies.

Don't be too tidy. Allow things to go a bit wild – even a few weeds are good. Let things die back naturally with the seasons, and remember to leave the seedheads on your plants after they have flowered.

Once you start, you will find yourself looking out for bird visitors every day, so it will be worth starting a diary. **Make a note of which birds you see feeding on which plants.**

After Christmas, ask a grown up if they have a spare pocket diary they don't want. You could use that as your bird buffet diary.

Dad gave me an old note-book, which I use as a bird diary.

93

Make a Willow Wigwam

Willow is a flexible and cheap material. It has been used for thousands of years to weave all sorts of things: baskets, sculptures, even small buildings!

If you push a freshly cut stem of willow into the ground in winter, it is likely to take root and grow into a new tree! This is called a hardwood cutting, and you can also do it with currant bushes and dogwoods!

Growing new plants from bits you have cut off is called "taking a cutting".

If you push lots of willow stems into the ground you can make a den or wigwam, and in the spring it will start to grow! These look excellent in the garden all year round, particularly in the winter, and in spring you could also grow things up them.

How to do it

Ask a grown-up to help you!

NOTE FOR GROWN-UPS: There are lots of places to buy willow rods online. Try searching under 'willow rods' or 'willow wigwam'. There is also a book: *Living Willow Sculpture* by John Warnes published by Search Press.

You will need:
- Sharp secateurs
- 10 or more willow stems – each one about 2cm thick and 1.5m long.
- Garden wire or twine.

1. Push the ends of five or six of the tallest stems into the ground so they form a circle of 'legs'.

2. Bind the stems together where they meet at the top with wire or twine to form a pyramid or cone.

3. Weave the remaining stems horizontally in and out of the willow 'legs' to form hoops or a spiral along the length of the cone. Snip off any untidy ends and fix with wire if you need to.

4. Your wigwam is finished! You can either keep it planted so that it will grow, or let it dry out so that in spring you can use it as a support for climbing plants like sweet peas or runner beans.

Where did you put your wigwam? Draw a picture or take a photo of your wigwam and stick it in here:

I planted a group of wigwams in circle. They are all different sizes and look funny!

Try your hand at hardwood cuttings

Many plants will grow roots from cuttings but only some grow from hardwood. Try cutting biggish stems of various different plants, like in the picture opposite. Leave them poked into the ground, in a bucket of soil, or in a jar of water to see what happens.

If you put your stems in a jar or bucket of water, you may notice little roots forming underwater. You can carefully plant them in pots of damp compost if you want to keep them growing.

Remember to plant the right way up. Plants tend to only grow roots from the bit that was nearest the ground in the first place!

Be a Tree Detective

In winter most trees do not have any leaves and it is difficult to tell what they are. Imagine you are a tree detective on a special mission to discover the secret winter identities of the trees.

There are all sorts of ways to find a tree's secret identity. Hunt under them for conkers, acorns or other seeds. Looking at bark, buds, and the shape of the tree can also give you clues.

Oak tree

Easy to spot by the clusters of scaly buds at the tip of each twig. Other buds are spread down the stem in a zig-zag pattern. **Draw a zig zag from bud to bud in the picture.**

Under the tree you should find lots of old oak leaves and acorns (see pages 12 and 33).

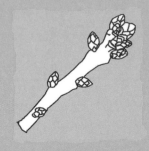

Stick a name label on the tree when you find out what it is!

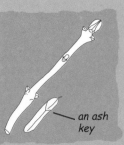

— an ash key

Ash tree

Can you see the pairs of coal-black buds and smooth grey bark? Sometimes there are big bunches of seeds or 'keys' hanging from the ends of the branches. These look like sycamore seeds (see page 72) with only one wing.

Horse chestnut tree

These have great big sticky leaf buds, and little triangular scars where the old leaves were. The scars look just like horseshoes. **Can you see the nails?**

You will also find lots of old conkers and conker shells under the tree.

Lime tree

The buds and young stems are shiny, orangey brown, and smooth. The buds hold a cunning clue to the tree's identity: they have only two scales and one is much bigger than the other.

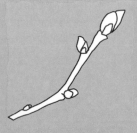

winter

Beech tree

The long, pointy buds of beech trees are the shape of really thin paintbrushes (only scaly, not hairy!) The ground is often covered with a thick layer of beech nuts, which are little woody cups.

Birch tree

Play detective and hunt down a tree with bark that is whitish and peeling. In late winter, you may spot lots of yellow catkins on the branches. The small buds are in a zig-zag pattern, just like an oak, but the twigs are thin and delicate-looking.

What are buds?

Buds are very tight packages that contain the coming year's leaves and flowers. In spring, the buds burst open and the tree comes into leaf.

When fruit farmers prune or cut their trees back in winter, to stop them growing too big, they know the difference between buds that will form fruit and buds that will just form leaves. This stops them from cutting off all of the next year's fruit.

These two pictures show apple tree buds. The one on the left shows leaf buds, which are small and only grow leaves. The one on the right shows fruit buds, which are much fatter, and grow leaves and flowers as well as fruit.

How do you think the picture will look in three or four months' time? **Draw on the leaves and flowers.**

What is brown and sticky? A stick!

97

Plan a Garden

Making a garden is about more than just sticking in some plants. You need to make sure that things are happy where they grow – or they might die.

A Chelsea Flower Show garden plan

You also have to make sure that there is something going on all year round. A garden can look wonderful in March and April with lots of spring bulbs, but it would look very sad and boring in June and July if there were no roses or clematis. Winter gardens are dull and brown without evergreens, colourful stems, and winter flowers.

Draw an outline of your own garden in this box below and mark on:
- where the walls and fences are
- where there are trees and evergreen plants
- any ponds or streams
- draw a compass on the plan to show which way is north
- draw a scale, so you know how big the garden is

NAME OF GARDEN: . . . .

NAME OF DESIGNER: . . . . DATE: . . . .

Winter

Draw in some of the following things to make your new garden:

Fountain   Perennials   Bulbs   Trees   Shrubs   Lawn
Statue   Vegetables   Climbers   Sun umbrella
Large grasses   Smelly herbs   Annuals   Table and chairs

Will it be a hot garden or cool garden?

Hot gardens have lots of reds, oranges and yellows.
Cool gardens are full of blues, whites and purples.

Green gardens were once very fashionable – they were usually made
of clipped evergreens, and large ponds and fountains. You might have
got a few white flowers if you were lucky!

Cottage gardens are a cheerful mixture of old fashioned plants in all
sorts of colours. They are happy, untidy, and full of bees!

What plants should I grow?

Perennials are plants that die back in winter and grow again the
next year. They look great in summer but are not much fun in winter.
Daylilies and anemones are perennials.

Evergreens are plants that do not lose their leaves. They are very
important to give the garden structure and shape in winter. Holly, ivy,
box, yew, and pine trees are all evergreens.

Annual plants grow from seed every year. They do not live long but
they are good for filing in gaps and changing the scenery. Nasturtiums,
sweet peas, and marigolds are annuals.

Bushes and trees are useful because they add height and make shade.

Bulbs are handy because they flower when they are
needed then vanish back into the ground afterwards.
Snowdrops and daffodils are bulbs.

Climbers are used to hide ugly walls and fences. They
can also grow into other plants. Clematis and ivy are
climbers.

Some plants are nice to touch, smell or listen to. Grasses
move and rustle in the wind, lambs ears are soft to touch
and stroke, and lavender and rosemary leaves smell lovely
and can be used in cooking.

I call
bushes 'shrubs'.
Do you?

99

A Watery Experiment

Plants need water just like we do. Rainwater goes into the roots of the plant and travels up the stem to the leaves and flowers. Then the water evaporates back into the air. This process is called *transpiration*.

The water moves up the stem in a bundle of little pipes called *xylem*. The plant can also suck up food from the soil, if it is dissolved in the water.

Fact: Water is sticky! Each tiny molecule of water sticks to all the others. If you pull on one, all the rest follow – this is why you can drink through a straw.

How to show that water moves up a plant

Cut your flower and put it in the jar of water. Add a few drops of food colouring. Leave it for a day or two to see what happens.

How long does the drink of coloured water take to get to the flower?

You will need:
- A jam jar or glass
- A white or light-coloured flower
- Some food colouring (try red or blue!)
- Water
- Ruler (optional)
- Clock (optional)

Try repeating the experiment in different ways:

– If the stem is twice as long, how much longer does the colour take to reach the flower?

– How about if you put the flower somewhere warm?

Winter

100

Have a flower race with a friend

Does water mover faster in some plants than others?

Repeat the experiment on the opposite page, but this time with two different flowers.

Take a trip to your local florist to see what they have that you could use.

Try daffodils, tulips, or snowdrops, or a big white lily like the one shown in the picture.

Make sure the stems are the same length, or one plant will get a head start!

Record your results here:

Time taken for colouring to reach flower:

Flower 1 . . . .

Flower 2 . . . .

What flowers did you use?

. . . .

Which flower was the winner?

. . . .

Now you have completed the experiment, look at the petals closely. Can you see a pattern of veins? What does that remind you of?

For water and dissolved food to get to where it is needed in the leaves and flowers, it must travel through a feathery network, a bit like the way blood travels through our veins.

Fact: Leaves have little holes or pores in them called *stomata*. This is where the water gets out of the plant once it has passed through. The stomata close at night and when the plant needs water.

Visit the Garden at ROSEMOOR

The RHS Garden at Rosemoor in Devon was given to the RHS in 1988. At that time, it was a relatively small garden surrounded by farmland. In just over two years, the farmland was converted into a much larger garden. It wasn't an easy job, but now the garden looks as though it has been there forever!

A visit to Rosemoor is worthwhile at any time of year. In winter, the frosts come down and settle in this pretty, wooded valley, and the gardeners work hard to make sure there is plenty to enjoy.

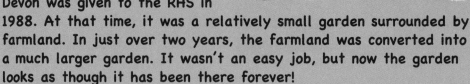

If you cannot get to Rosemoor, you can still complete these activities – see page 110 for a list of gardens to visit in your area.

Winter stems and bark

A lot of the colour in winter comes not from flowers, but from branch stems and tree trunks. They can be red, white, black, brown, yellow, orange, green, or pink. **How many can you find?**

The picture opposite shows the patterned bark of a plane tree.

See if you can find some interesting bark in the garden. Draw a picture of it in the space opposite, or if you prefer, take a bark rubbing or a photo and stick in with some glue.

Winter

The Winter Garden

Lady Anne Berry, the founder of the garden at Rosemoor, grew many colourful winter plants around the garden. You can find them all over it, as long as you know what to look for – look for leaves and stems, as well as winter flowers. Ask a gardener to point some out to you. Once you get the hang of it, **see how many winter flowers you can find and record them in the table below:**

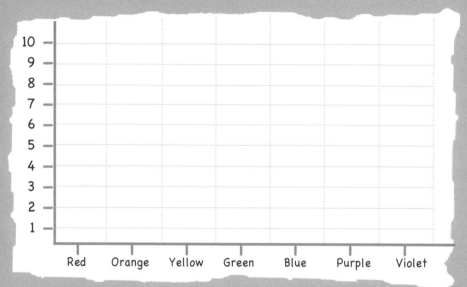

	Red	Orange	Yellow	Green	Blue	Purple	Violet

(graph with vertical axis numbered 1 to 10)

Everlasting evergreens

At this time of year it is easy to see which plants keep their leaves over winter. This is why they are called evergreens. **See if you can spot these three different types:**

EVERGREEN SHRUB
Date spotted:

. . . .

CONIFER
Date spotted:.

. . . .

PALM
Date spotted:

. . . .

Places to go

Visit the Glasshouse at WISLEY

The RHS built this new glasshouse at their garden at Wisley in Surrey. It was opened in June 2007 by The Queen.

The huge, cathedral-like glass structure uses bendy panes of glass to cover an area the same size as ten tennis courts. Inside are three climatic zones: Tropical, Moist Temperate, and Dry Temperate.

On a cold winter day, this is the place to be. It's always warm in the glasshouse – otherwise the plants will die – and in the Tropical Zone it's positively hot and sweaty. Come on in!

If you cannot get to the glasshouse at Wisley, try visiting a garden with one near your home, or when you are on holiday.

The comfortable zone

Warm Temperate climates really are the place to be if you don't like cold weather. There is no frost, so the plants can grow all year round, and you always get plenty of warm, sunny weather. If you have ever been to the Mediterranean on holiday, you will have a good idea what it's like. Not bad!

Hibiscus flower

You might recognise some of the plants in the Moist Temperate Zone. Perhaps you grow them at home as houseplants, or outdoors in the garden in the summer. Or maybe you saw them on holiday.

Draw one here. ⤸

Winter

Welcome to the desert

We call it the Dry Temperate Zone, but in places like this, where there is very little rain, you get desert conditions.

Can you name three deserts?

1. . . . .

2. . . . .

3. . . . .

A cactus in flower

Just look at the plants here! Most of them have juicy stems and leaves, which they use to store valuable water.

Most of the cacti are covered with nasty spines; in the wild, this is useful, as it stops thirsty animals from chewing them up as a juicy snack.

In winter, many of the plants in this zone may be in flower. If you are a desert plant, this is a good time to flower as it is relatively cool and it is more likely to rain.

It's tropical in the jungle

Tropical climates are home to the great rainforests of the world. You may know the adventures of Mowgli in *The Jungle Book*, or the story of Tarzan. These were set in the jungle, which is another word for rainforest.

Tropical orchid

Rainforest plants love it hot, wet, and steamy. They are always lush and green, and they often grow very quickly indeed. Some grow into very tall trees, while others produce the most amazing flowers and fruit.

Have an explore. What can you find? **Draw some of your favourite things here.** ⤳

Winter Quiz

This is a quiz designed to test your knowledge of the garden in winter. It is also meant to be a bit of fun, so not all the questions are difficult or have definite answers. You will find answers to some of the questions at the back of the book.

1. What is a parasite?

. . . .

2. How does mistletoe distribute its seeds?

. . . .

3. Holly and Ivy are both used as names for girls

Can you think of any more plants that are used as names?

Write them here:

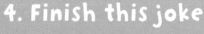

Are any used for boys?

4. Finish this joke

What did the snowman say when he sat on a holly leaf?

. . . . !

Winter

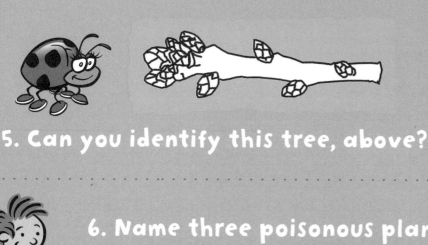

5. Can you identify this tree, above?

....

6. Name three poisonous plants

1. ....

2. ....

3. ....

7. Name two things we can do to help birds in winter

1. ....

2. ....

8. The aliens have landed!

When you woke up this morning there was a spaceship on your lawn. The aliens are chilly and rather confused. Last time they were here everything was warm and green. Explain what has happened in the space below using pictures and numbers.

9. Find the following words in this grid

Frost   Snow   Christmas tree   Holly   Fleece
Hibernate   Evergreen   Presents   Birdfood   Winter

C	A	R	H	F	D	O	O	F	D	R	I	B
H	Z	N	U	B	L	W	Z	E	V	O	Y	P
R	C	L	P	K	G	E	D	K	S	N	O	W
I	B	C	N	J	H	D	E	X	I	C	D	E
S	T	R	M	O	K	U	V	C	J	P	I	G
T	A	S	L	J	I	R	E	S	E	N	K	S
M	I	L	G	D	Y	V	R	N	T	P	R	F
A	Y	E	Q	P	K	F	G	V	N	O	E	R
S	X	D	T	L	L	R	R	X	J	H	A	O
T	J	E	T	A	N	R	E	B	I	H	S	S
R	C	A	D	O	D	I	E	Q	E	V	C	T
E	F	E	R	L	W	I	N	T	E	R	Q	M
E	C	S	P	R	E	S	E	N	T	S	Z	S
M	S	R	G	R	N	B	E	E	W	E	S	L

10. You are the editor of a gardening magazine and have received this letter

Reply to the reader on this piece of paper, explaining what the problem might be.

Dear Editor,
I have a holly tree in my garden and it is beautiful but it never has any berries. Please help!

Yours faithfully,

Mr Smallhoe

My Winter Garden

Draw you ideal winter garden containing all the things you like about winter. What is there to look at now the summer flowers have gone? What makes it an exciting place to be? Don't forget to feed the birds!

Gardens to Visit

All the gardens listed below are friendly to children and some have special family events. Most gardens, however, are exciting places for children to explore; visit **www.rhs.org.uk/ rhsgardenfinder/gardenfinder.asp** for a much larger list.

Floors Castle & Gardens, Roxburghshire. www.floorscastle.com
Scone Palace, Perthshire. www.scone-palace.net
Alnwick Garden, Northumberland www.alnwickgarden.com
Holker Hall Garden, Cumbria. www.holker-hall.co.uk
Muncaster Castle Garden, Cumbria. www.muncaster.co.uk
Burton Agnes Gardens, E. Yorkshire. www.burton-agnes.co.uk
Newby Hall & Gardens, N. Yorkshire. www.newbyhall.co.uk
RHS Garden Harlow Carr, N. Yorkshire. www.rhs.org.uk/WhatsOn/index.htm
Ripley Castle & Garden, North Yorkshire. www.ripleycastle.co.uk
Thorp Perrow Arboretum, North Yorkshire. www.thorpperrow.com
Doddington Hall & Gardens, Lincolnshire. www.doddingtonhall.com
Normanby Hall Country Park, Lincolnshire. www.northlincs.gov.uk/normanby
Arley Hall & Gardens, Cheshire. www.arleyhallandgardens.com
Ness Botanic Garden, Cheshire. www.nessgardens.org.uk
Fairhaven Woodland & Water Garden, Norfolk. www.fairhavengarden.co.uk
Renishaw Hall Gardens, Derbyshire. www.sitwell.co.uk
Garden Organic Ryton, Warwickshire. www.gardenorganic.org.uk/gardens/ryton.php
Ragley Hall, Warwickshire. www.ragleyhall.com
Blenheim Palace, Oxfordshire. www.blenheimpalace.com
Living Rainforest, Berkshire. www.livingrainforest.org
Hatfield House, Hertfordshire. www.hatfield-house.co.uk
RHS Garden Wisley, Surrey. www.rhs.org.uk/WhatsOn/index.htmp
RHS Garden Hyde Hall, Essex. www.rhs.org.uk/WhatsOn/index.htm
Bedgebury Pinetum, Kent. www.bedgeburypinetum.org.uk
Penshurst Place & Gardens, Kent. www.penshurstplace.com
Garden Organic Yalding, Kent. www.gardenorganic.org.uk/gardens/yalding.php
Batsford Arboretum, Gloucestershire. www.batsford-arboretum.co.uk
Westonbirt National Arboretum, Gloucestershire. www.forestry.gov.uk/westonbirt
Wilton House, Wiltshire. www.wiltonhouse.co.uk
Bicton Park Botanical Gardens, Devon. www.bictongardens.co.uk
RHS Garden Rosemoor, Devon. www.rhs.org.uk/WhatsOn/index.htm
Hestercombe, Somerset. www.hestercombe.com
Eden Project, Cornwall. www.edenproject.com
The Lost Gardens of Heligan, Cornwall. www.heligan.com
Trebah Garden, Cornwall. www.trebahgarden.co.uk
National Botanic Garden of Wales, Carmarthenshire. www.gardenofwales.org.uk
Picton Castle Gardens, Pembrokeshire. www.pictoncastle.co.uk
Carnfunnock Country Park, Co. Antrim. www.larne.gov.uk/carnfunnock.html

Useful links

The websites below will allow you to explore the world of gardening and nature even further. Those marked * have special areas for children, such as projects and games.

*ROYAL HORTICULTURAL SOCIETY www.rhs.org.uk/explorers

*BBC GARDENING www.bbc.co.uk/gardening/gardening_with_children

GARDEN ORGANIC www.gardenorganic.org.uk

*KEW GARDENS www.kew.org/climbersandcreepers/home.html

NATURAL ENGLAND www.naturalengland.org.uk

*NATURAL HISTORY MUSEUM www.nhm.ac.uk/nature-online

*NATURE'S CALENDAR www.naturescalendar.org.uk

*NATURE DETECTIVES www.naturedetectives.org.uk

THE WILDLIFE TRUSTS www.wildlifetrusts.org

THE WOODLAND TRUST www.woodland-trust.org.uk

FEDERATION OF CITY FARMS www.farmgarden.org.uk

*RSPB KIDS www.rspb.org.uk/youth

WIGGLY WRIGGLERS www.wigglywigglers.co.uk

CJ WILDBIRD FOODS www.birdfood.co.uk

UK SAFARI www.uksafari.com

BUGLIFE www.buglife.org.uk

Quiz Answers

SPRING: 2. water/sun/soil or earth; 3. because they are stripy; 4. (a) Japan, (b) yellow, (c) the plant is scented, (d) they are large; 8. (a) pollen, (b) because there are more flowers in spring.

SUMMER: 1. see p.42; 2. eggs/caterpillars/nectar/hibernate; 3. greenfly and blackfly; 4. false; 5. lavender/nasturtium/violet; 6. false; 8. see pp.48-49; 9. green/acorn/rain/dandelion/earthworm/nettle - spells GARDEN.

AUTUMN: 1. (a) old man's beard or traveller's joy, (b) so they can be blown around in the wind; 2. true; 3. (a) its hooks hold onto animals as they pass by, (b) its wings allow the seed to spin like a helicopter so it can fly; 4. fly agaric; 5. see opposite; 6. it is too cold and dark; 9. false

WINTER: 1. something that gets some or all of its food from another living thing and gives nothing in return; 2. birds wipe them onto branches; 5. oak; 7. see pp.92-93

Become an RHS Garden Explorer

Joining the RHS Garden Explorers opens up a world of exciting events, hands-on gardening and benefits for all the family. Enjoy exclusive Garden Explorer events and days out, including trails, gardening activity packs and family friendly fun.

When you join, each RHS Garden Explorer in your family will receive a Welcome Pack*, which includes:

- The 'RHS Garden Explorers' Handbook'
- Seeds
- A seasonal Plant Passport with Stamper Pen
- 'Dig and Discover' Newsletter – three times a year.

You will also receive:

- Free entry to RHS Gardens for 2 adults and up to 4 children
- Free monthly magazine 'The Garden' (RRP £4.25)
- Free Gardening Advisory Service
- Exclusive entry and reduced rate tickets to RHS Flower Shows
- Free access to over 140 Recommended Gardens throughout their opening season or at selected periods**
- Free use of the RHS Garden Explorers Activity Pack at each RHS Garden. An updated pack will be available each season.
- Free garden-based events exclusively for RHS Garden Explorers
- Quarterly email updates

For further information, to join and for games and gardening activities visit:
www.rhs.org.uk/explorers

*Up to two children receive Garden Explorers Welcome Packs, additional packs can be provided at an additional cost

**Only cardholder 1 has free access to RHS Recommended Gardens

Acknowledgements

RHS Garden Explorer logo and characters by Chris Wray
Other illustrations by Artful Doodlers and Simon Maughan

All photos copyright © Royal Horticultural Society, unless listed below:

Clay Perry/RHS: 6, 7, 13bl, 13br, 23t, 24c, 24b, 26cl, 49t, 49cb, 51ut, 51lt, 51ct, 58, 59, 61, 62, 63, 65bl, 66t, 68trt, 68trc, 68trb, 76tr, 76cr, 76cl, 76br, 76bl, 77tl, 85, 87, 93tr, 103bl, 103bc, 104b, 10t, 105b **Mike Grant/RHS Herbarium:** 10t, 26br **Maddy Aldiss:** 9c **CJ Birdfoods:** 20t, 20ct, 20c, 20cb, 20b, 92trt, 92trc, 92trb **Niki Simpson:** 22bc, 84 **Naomi Slade:** 26c, 44, 45b, 50t, 51b, 100, 101 **The Harry Smith Collection:** 26cr **Wriggly Wrigglers:** 29t, 74tr, 75tr **Noel Cornwall:** 38bc **Simon Maughan:** 43c, 43cr, 48b, 49ct, 49c, 52t, 52c, 52cb, 52bl, 53l, 67b, 70tr, 70br, 71t, 71ct, 71b, 72tr, 72cr, 72bl, 80c, 80b, 95bl **Neil Hepworth/RHS:** 65c **Martin Bramwell/RHS:** 68cl, 68cr, 68bl **Tim Sandall/RHS:** 70bl, 72tl, 86, 93tc, 94t, 95br **Ann For Fungi:** 79tr **Helen Bostock/RHS:**91 **Rose Cooper:** 103br **Paul Upward/RHS:** 104t

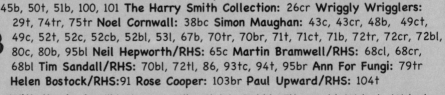

With thanks to Niki Simpson, Mike Sleigh, Debbie Fitzgerald, Wriggly Wrigglers (www.wigglywigglers.co.uk), and CJ Wildbird Foods (www.birdfood.co.uk) for their help with photography.